Readers Love Denise's Playful Math Books

"These games are great for using and practicing maths skills in a context in which there is some real motivation to do so. I love how they provide opportunities to explore a wide variety of approaches, including number bonds and logical thinking.

"My children are always pleased, even excited, when I suggest one of these games. Sometimes they even ask to play them unprompted!"
—MIRANDA JUBB, ONLINE READER REVIEW

"It revolutionized our homeschool this year."
—CAITLIN FITZPATRICK CURLEY, MY-LITTLE-POPPIES.COM

"I have played several of these games with my son, and each one was met with delight on his part and the sharing of delightful conversation about numbers and thinking between us.

"I love what Gaskins has to say about working with your children as opposed to simply assigning them work to do. This sums up the philosophy that I try to keep forefront in our home.

"Highly, highly recommended."
—AMY, HOPE IS THE WORD BLOG

"Wonderful games for elementary students. The author includes a link for printable game boards, ensuring that I don't spend more time making games than playing them.

"Variations for each game = SO many ways to explore numbers.

"You will love this book."
—MARISA, ONLINE READER REVIEW

COMBINED VOLUME: TWO BOOKS IN ONE

Math You Can Play Combo

Number Games
for Young Learners

Denise Gaskins

Tabletop Academy Press

Tabletop Academy Press, Blue Mound, IL, USA
tabletopacademy.net

ISBN: 978-1-892083-21-0
Library of Congress Control Number: 2016912985

CREDITS:

Portions of this book were originally published on the Let's Play Math blog.
DeniseGaskins.com

Cover photos by Charles Schmidt and Zeljko Santrac via iStock:
istockphoto.com/photo/card-game-13139491
istockphoto.com/photo/family-game-16247492

Riffle shuffle photo by Johnny Blood (CC-BY-SA 2.0):
commons.wikimedia.org/wiki/File:Riffle_shuffle.jpg

Author photo by Christina Vernon:
melliru.com

The amazement I felt at the age of seven
  when realizing
    that counting to one hundred twice
      is the same as counting to two hundred once

was no less than when as a sophomore in college
  I discovered I could prove
    that the set of non-intersecting circles in a plane
      is countable.

— BARRY GARELICK

Contents

Preface to the *Math You Can Play* Series

THE PLAYFUL, PUZZLE-SOLVING SIDE OF math has always attracted me. In elementary school, calculations were a tedious chore, but word problems provided the opportunity to try out my deductive powers. High school algebra and geometry were exercises in logical reasoning, and college physics was one story problem after another—great fun!

As my children grew, I wanted to share this sort of mathematical play with them, but the mundane busyness of everyday life kept pushing aside my good intentions. Determined to make it happen, I found a way to defeat procrastination: invite friends to bring their kids over for a math playdate. We grappled with problems, solved puzzles, and shared games. Skeptical at first, the kids soon looked forward to math club. When that gang grew up and moved on, their younger siblings came to play, and others after them. Sometimes we met weekly, sometimes monthly or just off and on. At our house, at the library, in the park—more than twenty years of playing math with kids.

Now I've gathered our favorite math club games into these *Math You Can Play* books. They are simple to learn, easy to set up, and quick to play, so even the busiest parents can build their children's mental math skills and promote logical thinking.

I hope you enjoy these games as much as we have. If you have any questions, I would love to hear from you.

—DENISE GASKINS
LETSPLAYMATH@GMAIL.COM

Acknowledgements

No man is an island, entire of itself.
Every man is a piece of the continent, a part of the main.
If a clod be washed away by the sea,
Europe is the less, as well as if a promontory were.

—JOHN DONNE

Neither an island nor a promontory—I am that little clod supported by a continent of family, friends, and online acquaintances whose help and encouragement have made my math books possible. I cannot express the debt I owe to my husband David, whose patience stretches far beyond what I deserve, and our children, who taught me so much over the many years of homeschooling.

Thank you to Marilyn Kok and Sue Kunzeman, who brought their children to that first math playdate—and kept bringing them back. Special thanks to the many math club kids who joined in the activities and tested out the games. Thank you to John Golden, whose Math Hombre blog inspires me to think deeply about math games, and to Sue VanHattum, whose work on her own book, *Playing With Math: Stories from Math Circles, Homeschoolers, and Passionate Teachers*, convinced me to bring my books back into print. To my many thousands of book and blog readers, your comments have kept me going. To my fellow math bloggers, I've learned so much from you all!

Fervent thanks to my beta readers: Becky, Emily, Jennifer, Katie, Laura, Marcia, Maria, Marisa, Roxana, Sharon, Siobhan, and Sue.

And unending gratitude to my friend and editor Robin Netherton. Whatever mistakes remain are due to my continual tinkering with the text after it left her hands.

Math is the beautiful,
    rich,
        joyful,
            playful,
                surprising,
            frustrating,
        humbling,
    and creative art
that speaks to something transcendental.

It is worthy of much exploration and examination
because it is intrinsically beautiful,
    nothing more to say.

Why play the violin?
Because it is beautiful!

Why engage in math?
Because it, too, is beautiful!

—JAMES TANTON

A Strategy for Learning

There should be no element of slavery in learning. Enforced exercise does no harm to the body, but enforced learning will not stay in the mind. So avoid compulsion, and let your children's lessons take the form of play.
—Plato

Introduction: How to Use This Book

If a perfect teacher developed the ideal teaching strategy, what would it be like?

♦ An ideal teaching strategy would have to be flexible, working in a variety of situations with students of all ages.

♦ It would promote true understanding and reasoning skills, not mere regurgitation of facts.

♦ It would prepare children to learn on their own.

♦ Surely the ideal teaching strategy would be enjoyable, perhaps even so much fun that the students don't realize they are learning.

♦ And it would be simple enough that imperfect teachers could use it, too.

This is idle speculation, of course. TNo teaching strategy works with every student in every subject. But for math, at least, there is a wonderful way to stimulate our children's number skills and encourage them to think: we can play games.

Math games push students to develop a creatively logical approach to solving problems. When children play games, they build reasoning skills that will help them throughout their lives. In the stress-free struggle of a game, players learn to analyze situations and draw conclusions. They must consider their options, change their plans in reaction to the other player's moves, and look for the less obvious solutions in order to outwit their opponents.

Even more important, games help children learn to enjoy the challenge of thinking hard. Children willingly practice far more arithmetic than they would suffer through on a workbook page. Their vocabulary grows as they discuss options and strategies with their fellow players. Because their attention is focused on their next move, they don't notice how much they are learning.

And games are good medicine for math anxiety. Everyone knows it takes time to master the fine points of a game, so children can make mistakes or "get stuck" without losing face.

If your child feels discouraged or has an "I can't do it" attitude toward math, try taking him off the textbooks for a while. Feed him a strict diet of games. It will not be long before his eyes regain their sparkle. Beating a parent at a math game will give any child confidence. And if you're like me, your kids will beat you more often than you might want to admit.

Math You Can Play

Clear off a table, find a deck of cards, and you're ready to enjoy some math. Most of the games in this book take only a few minutes to play, so they fit into your most hectic days.

In three decades of teaching, I've noticed that flexibility with mental calculation is one of the best predictors of success in high school math and beyond. So the *Math You Can Play* games will stretch your children's ability to manipulate numbers in their heads. But unlike the typical "computerized flash card" games online, most of these games will also encourage your children to think strategically, to compare different options in choosing their moves.

"Be careful! There are a lot of useless games out there," says math professor and blogger John Golden. "Look for problem solving, the need for strategy, and math content.

"The best games offer equal opportunity (or nearly so) to all your students. Games that require computational speed to be successful will disenfranchise instead of engage your students who need the game the most."

Each book in the *Math You Can Play* series features twenty or more of my favorite math games, offering a variety of challenges for all ages. If you are a parent, these games provide opportunities to enjoy quality time with your children. If you are a classroom teacher, use the games as warm-ups and learning center activities or for a relaxing review day at the end of a term. If you are a tutor or homeschooler, make games a regular feature in your lesson plans to build your students' mental math skills.

Know that my division of these games by grade level is inherently arbitrary. Children may eagerly play a game with advanced concepts if the fun of the challenge outweighs the work involved. Second- or third-grade students can enjoy some of the games in the prealgebra book. On the other hand, don't worry that a game is too easy for your students, as long as they find it interesting. Even college students will enjoy a round of Farkle (in the addition book) or Wild and Crazy Eights (a childhood classic from the counting book). An easy game lets the players focus most of their attention on the logic of strategy.

As Peggy Kaye, author of *Games for Math*, writes: "Children learn more math and enjoy math more if they play games that are a little too easy rather than a little too hard."

Games give children a meaningful context in which to think about and manipulate numbers, shapes, and patterns, so they help players of all skill levels learn together. As children play, they exchange ideas and insights.

"Games can allow children to operate at different levels of thinking and to learn from each other," says education researcher Jenni Way.

"In a group of children playing a game, one child might be encountering a concept for the first time, another may be developing his/her understanding of the concept, a third consolidating previously learned concepts."

Talk with Your Kids

The modern world is a slave to busyness. Marketers tempt well-intentioned parents with toys and apps that claim to build academic skills while they keep our children occupied. Homeschoolers dream of finding a curriculum that will let the kids teach themselves. And even the most attentive teachers may hope that game time will give them a chance to correct papers or catch up on lesson plans.

Be warned: although children can play these games on their own, they learn much more when we adults play along.

When adults play the game, we reinforce the value of mathematical play. By giving up our time, we prove that we consider this just as important as *[insert whatever we would have been doing]*. If the game is worthy of our attention, then it becomes more attractive to our children.

Also, it is only as we watch our kids' responses and listen to their comments during the course of the game that we discover what they understand about math. Where do they get confused? What do they do when they are stuck? Can they use the number relationships they do remember to figure out something they don't know? How easily do they give up?

"Language should be part of the activity," says math teacher and author Claudia Zaslavsky. "*Talk* while you and your child are playing games. Ask questions that encourage your child to describe her actions and explain her conclusions."

Real education, learning that sticks for a lifetime, comes through person-to-person interactions. Our children absorb more from the give and take of simple discussion with an adult than from even the best workbook or teaching video.

If you're not sure how to start a conversation about math, browse the stories at Christopher Danielson's Talking Math with Your Kids blog.[†]

As homeschooler Lucinda Leo explains, "With any curriculum there is the temptation to leave a child to get on with the set number of pages while you get on with something else. My long-term goal is for my kids to be independent learners, but the best way for that to happen is for me to be by their side now, enjoying puzzles and stories, asking good questions and modelling creative problem-solving strategies."

And playing math games.

Mixing It Up

Games evolve as they move from one person to another. Where possible, I have credited each game's inventor and told a bit of its history. But some games have been around so long they are impossible for me to trace. Many are variations on traditional childhood favorites. For example, I was playing Tens Concentration (page 85) with my math club kids years before I read about it in Constance Kamii's *Young Children Reinvent Arithmetic*. Similarly, an uncountable number of parents and teachers have played Math War (page 90) with their students; a few of my variations are original, but the underlying idea is far from new.

Or consider the lineage of Forty-Niners (page 138). First someone invented dice, and generations of players created a multitude of folk games, culminating in Pig (page 137). Using cards instead of dice and adding a Wild West theme, James Ernest created the Gold Digger variation and gave it away at his website. Teachers wanted their students to practice with bigger numbers, so they tried a regular deck of playing cards, and the game became Stop or Dare at the Nrich web-

---

[†] *I'll refer to dozens of blogs, websites, and other resources throughout this book. All of these (and more) are listed in the appendix "Quotes and Reference Links" on page 170.*

site. For my version, I increased the risk level by turning all the face cards into bandits and adding the jokers as claim jumpers.

Game rules are a social convention, easy to change by agreement among the players. Feel free to invent your own rules, and encourage your children to modify the games as they play.

For instance:

♦ Can you make the game easier, so young children can play? Or harder, to challenge adults?

♦ What would happen if you changed the number of moves? Or the number of cards you draw, or how many dice you throw?

♦ Can you invent a story to explain the game—like James Ernest did with Gold Digger—or tie it to a favorite book?

♦ If the game uses cards, can you figure out a way to play it with dice or dominoes? Or transfer it to a game board?

♦ If the game uses a number chart, could you play it on a clock or calendar instead? Or is there a way to use money in the game?

♦ Or can you change it into a whole-body action game? Perhaps using sidewalk chalk?

As children tinker with the game, they will be prompted to think more deeply about the math behind it.

Unschooling advocate Pam Sorooshian explains the connection between games and math this way:

Mathematicians don't sit around doing the kind of math that you learned in school. What they do is "play around" with number games, spatial puzzles, strategy, and logic.

They don't just play the same old games, though. They change the rules a little, and then they look at how the game changes.

So, when you play games, you are doing exactly what mathematicians really do—if you fool with the games a bit, exper-

iment, see how the play changes if you change a rule here and there. Oh, and when you make up games and they flop, be sure to examine why they flop — that is a big huge part of what mathematicians do, too.

Finally, although the point of these games is for children to practice mental math, please don't treat them as worksheets in disguise. A game should be voluntary and fun. No matter how good it sounds to you, if a game doesn't interest your kids, put it away. You can always try another one tomorrow.

You will know when you find the right game because your children will wear you out wanting to play it again and again and again.

1	2	3	4	5	6	7	8	9	10
11	12	13	14	15	16	17	18	19	20
21	22	23	24	25	26	27	28	29	30
31	32	33	34	35	36	37	38	39	40
41	42	43	44	45	46	47	48	49	50
51	52	53	54	55	56	57	58	59	60
61	62	63	64	65	66	67	68	69	70
71	72	73	74	75	76	77	78	79	80
81	82	83	84	85	86	87	88	89	90
91	92	93	94	95	96	97	98	99	100

You can play many games on a hundred chart. The *Number Game Printables Pack* includes 0–99 charts, too.

We do not stop playing because we grow old. We grow old because we stop playing.

—Anonymous

Gather Your Game Supplies

I have a limited amount of free time, and I don't want to spend it cutting out specialized game pieces or cards. A few games require printable cards or game boards, but most of the games in the *Math You Can Play* series use basic items you already have, such as playing cards and dice.

A Deck of Math Cards

Whenever a game calls for playing cards, I use an international standard poker- or bridge-style deck (or *pack;* the terms are interchangeable). There are fifty-two cards in four suits — spades (the pointy black shape), hearts, clubs (the clover shape), and diamonds — with thirteen cards per suit. The number cards range from the ace to ten, and each suit has three face cards called jack, queen, and king. Your deck may have one or two additional cards called jokers, which are not officially part of the deck but may be used for some games.

Math cards are simply the forty number cards (ace through ten in all four suits) from a standard deck. The ace counts as "one" in all math card games. Some game variations call for using the face cards as higher numbers: jack = 11, queen = 12, and king = 13. In a few games, we use the queens as zeros, because the Q is round enough for pretend.

Other types of card decks may work as well, so feel free to experiment with whatever you have on hand. For instance, Uno cards are numbered zero to nine, Phase 10 cards have one to twelve, and Rook cards go from one to fourteen. Rummikub tiles use the numbers one to thirteen. Most of the games in this book could be adapted to use any of these.

Game Boards

Many games use graph paper or a hundred chart, which you can easily find online. For most other games, hand-drawn boards work fine. One reason Tic-Tac-Toe is a perennial favorite is that children can draw the board whenever they want to play.

I've created a free PDF packet of charts and game boards called the *Number Game Printables Pack*, which you can download from my blog.[†] You may reproduce these for use within your own family, classroom, or homeschool group.

To save paper, you may wish to reuse game boards. Print the game board on cardstock and laminate it—I love my laminator!—or slip the printed game board into a clear (not frosted) page protector, adding a few extra sheets of card stock or the back of an old notebook for stiffness. Then your children can mark moves with dry-erase markers and wipe them clean with an old, dry cloth. Some of the colored dry-erase markers leave stains, but you can wash off stubborn marks with rubbing alcohol or window cleaner.

A very few games call for larger homemade boards. For example, Dinosaur Race (page 27) needs a simple track, twelve to twenty spaces long, and each space needs to be large enough for a couple of toy dinosaurs or other small figures. An open manila file folder can serve as a sturdy foundation on which to draw or paste the board, convenient for playing and easy to store. And if you keep a stack of blank manila folders freely available, your children will enjoy making up their own board games.

† *TabletopAcademy.net/Free-Printables*

Glue two manila folders together to make
an even bigger game board.

Other Bits and Pieces

Many games call for small toy figures or other items to mark the players' position or moves. If two different types of tokens are needed, you may borrow the pieces from a checkers game or try using pennies and nickels, milk jug lids in different colors, dried pinto and navy beans, or inexpensive glass gems from the craft section of your local department store.

When a game calls for dice, I have in mind the standard six-sided cubes with dots marking the numbers one through six. Most games only need one or two dice, but Farkle requires six. In many of the games, you may substitute higher-numbered dice for a greater challenge. And children enjoy using novelty dice when making up their own games.

A few games call for either a double-six or double-nine set of dominoes. If you are buying these, I recommend getting the larger set. You can always set aside the higher-numbered tiles when playing with young children.

Ready to Play?

If you want to put together a game box to keep all your supplies in one place, you will need:

- standard playing cards (two or more decks)
- pencils or pens
- colored felt-tip markers or colored pencils
- blank paper
- at least two kinds of tokens
- dice
- dominoes
- graph paper in assorted sizes[†]
- a couple of hundred charts[‡]

Try to let children learn by playing. Explain the rules as simply as possible and get right into the fun. You can add details, exceptions, and special situations as they come up during play or before starting future games. At our house, we play a few practice rounds first, and I make sure all the rules have been explained before we keep score.

Card games have a traditional ethic that guides players in choosing who gets to deal, who goes first, what to do if something goes wrong in the deal or during play, and more. If you are unsure about questions of this sort, read the appendix "Game-Playing Basics" on page 159.

Many of the game listings include suggestions for *house rules*, which are optional modifications of the game. The way a game is played varies from one place to another, and only a few tournament-style games have an official governing body to set the rules. If you're not playing in an official competition, then everything is negotiable. Players should make sure they agree on the rules before starting to play.

[†] *incompetech.com/graphpaper*
[‡] *themathworksheetsite.com/h_chart.html*

Counting & Number Bond Games

Early Counting

A child learns to count spoonfuls,
learns to count people,
    learns to count fingers,
        learns to just plain count,
and in the process acquires the abstract concept
    of, for example, "two."

The child takes ownership of this concept
and can reapply it freely.

As adults we may take "two" for granted,
but we have never met it,
    never touched it,
        never tasted it.

It is one of the first completely abstract concepts
that we ever owned.

              —JONATHAN HALABI

Quick Tip: It's Harder Than It Looks

For very young children, counting is a threefold challenge.

♦ Point to each item in your collection, without skipping or repeating any of them.

♦ Recite the counting numbers in order as you point, one per item, without missing or repeating any numbers.

♦ Recognize that the last number you say has a double meaning. It names that item (the *seventh* thing in my collection) and also tells how many items are in the group.

Mistakes are common in all three areas, so don't be surprised when your children get confused. The process will eventually come together in their minds.

Subitizing Cards

Subitizing ("soo-bit-izing") means being able to recognize at a glance how many items are in a group. Very young children can subitize groups of two or three, but counting the spots on a six-sided die is difficult for them. Adults can usually subitize up to four items and rely on counting, pattern recognition, or quick mental addition for larger numbers.

Normal playing cards can be even more confusing than dice because preschool children do not yet know (or consistently remember) the number symbols. And traditional playing cards include extra suit symbols next to each number, which are not supposed to be counted.

To avoid frustrating young children and distracting them from the game, I recommend that parents of preschoolers make a special set of subitizing cards. Take the aces, twos, and threes from a deck of cards. (You can save the rest of the cards to use as train cars for Number Train, page 29. Or convert them into a Euchre deck for older chil-

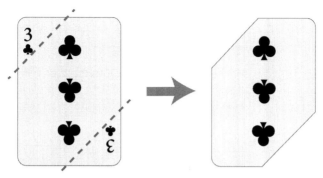

How many items do you see? Young children
don't know which shapes to ignore.

dren and adults.) Either cut off the corners or use white correction
fluid to cover the extra symbols. Keep these subitizing cards separate
from your other decks.

By the way, the written symbols for numbers are properly called
numerals. A numeral is related to its number as a street sign is related
to the street itself, or as your name is related to you, the person. I
remember suffering under pedantic elementary teachers who fussed
about correct usage during the New Math era of the 1960s. Most people speak informally, however, and use the word *number* in both cases.

Dotty Subitizing Cards

If you're feeling creative, make a special set of polka-dot subitizing
cards. You will need 12–18 blank index cards or several sheets of thick
paper cut into card-size pieces.

♦ Divide your blank cards into three piles.

♦ For the first pile, make one dot on each card. I like to use
a set of Bingo-style paint markers from the dollar store for
making big, colorful dots, or you can draw a circle and color
it in with a regular marker.

♦ For the second pile, make two dots per card, and put three
dots on each card in the third pile. On some cards you may

want to place the dots randomly. On others, follow the dots-in-a-row pattern used on dice and playing cards.

♦ After the marker paint is dry, you can laminate the cards for durability if you wish.

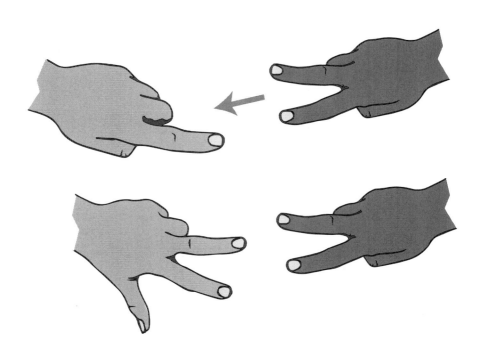

Chopsticks: When a two-points hand taps a one-point hand, that player must put out two more fingers.

Chopsticks

MATH CONCEPTS: counting up to five, thinking ahead.
PLAYERS: two or more.
EQUIPMENT: none.

How to Play

Each player starts with both hands as fists, palm down, pointer fingers extended to show one point for each hand. On your turn, use one of your fingers to tap one hand:

- If you tap an opponent's hand, that person must extend as many extra fingers on that hand (in addition to the points already there) as you have showing on the hand that tapped. Your own fingers don't change.

- If you force your opponent to extend all the fingers and thumb on one hand (five or more points), that makes a "dead hand." Dead hands go behind the player's back, out of the game.

- If you tap your own hand, you can "split" fingers from one hand to the other. For instance, if you have three points on one hand and only one on the other, you may tap hands to rearrange them, putting out two fingers on each hand. Splits do not have to end up even, but each hand must end up with at least one point (and less than five, of course).

- You may even revive a dead hand if you have enough fingers on your other hand to split. A dead hand has lost all its points, so it starts at zero. When you tap it, you can share out the points from your other hand as you wish.

The last player with a live hand wins the game.

Variations

HOUSE RULE: Do you want a shorter game? Omit the splits. Or you could allow ordinary splits but not splitting fingers to dead hands.

NUBS: All splits must share the fingers evenly between the hands. If you have an odd number of points, this will leave you with "half fingers," shown by curling those fingers down.

ZOMBIES: (For advanced players.) If a hand is tapped with more fingers than are needed to put it out of the game, it comes back from the dead with the leftover points. For instance, if you have four fingers out, and your opponent taps you with a two-finger hand, that would fill up your hand with one point left over. Close your fist, and then hold out just the zombie point. In this variation, the only way to kill a hand is to give it exactly five points.

History

Finger-counting games are common in eastern Asia—and they must be contagious, since my daughters caught them from their Korean friends at college. Middle school teacher Nico Rowinsky shared Chopsticks (which is simpler than the version my daughters brought home) in a comment on the "Tiny Math Games" post at Dan Meyer's blog.

Collect Ten

MATH CONCEPTS: subitizing, counting to ten.
PLAYERS: any number.
EQUIPMENT: subitizing cards (page 18), pile of tokens, a bowl for each player.

How to Play

Give each player a bowl or small basket. Place the pile of tokens (pennies, milk jug lids, cotton balls, or small toys) in the center, where all can reach. Shuffle and stack the cards or spread them face down into a fishing pond.

On your turn, draw a card and count that many tokens to put in your bowl. Very young children can count by matching tokens to their card, placing one on each symbol. Now count how many items you have collected so far. The first player to collect ten or more is the winner.

Variations

Make up a story to go with the game. You are collecting eggs on the farm, or you are robots picking out new gears and memory chips, or perhaps the goldfish have escaped from their bowl and need help getting back into the water.

As your child learns to count higher, let the target number grow. Can you collect fifteen or twenty?

GIVE AWAY: Start with ten tokens in your bowl. On each turn draw a card, and put that many tokens into a discard pile on the table. How many do you have left? The first player to get rid of all the tokens wins the game.

DOTTY ART: Provide extra-large sheets of construction paper and an assortment of bingo-style paint dot markers. When you draw a card, choose a color and add that many dots to your picture.

Up and Down the Stairs: The parent rolls a die or draws a card, and the child moves that many steps. Or have children start on the middle stair and move up for a black card and down for a red card. Will they ever get off the stairs?

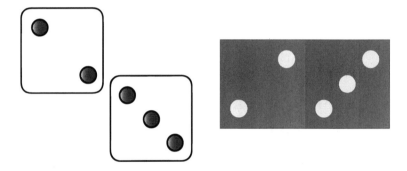

Domino Match: If you roll a two and three, then look for the domino tile with those numbers.

Domino Match

MATH CONCEPTS: counting to six, subitizing with dot patterns, visual memory, matching sets.
PLAYERS: two or more.
EQUIPMENT: one set of double-six dominoes, two six-sided dice.

How to Play

Set all domino tiles face up in the middle of the table. On your turn, roll the two dice and claim the domino tile that matches the dot patterns on both dice, unless that tile has already been taken by another player. With two players, the first to claim ten tiles wins the game. For three or more players, the goal is six tiles.

Variations

HOUSE RULE: How will you handle duplicate rolls? At our house, if your dice match a tile someone else has already claimed, you can "steal" that tile from the other player.

DOMINO COVER-UP: Each player needs a specific type or color of token. When there is no tile that matches both dice rolled, the player may put tokens on any two separate tiles, covering the matching numbers. On a future turn, the player may be able to claim one of these tiles by rolling the uncovered number.

History

Domino Cover-Up was created by Jean Carlton, lead teacher in the infant room at Old Dominion University Child Development Center, and shared by Alice P. Wakefield in *Early Childhood Number Games: Teachers Reinvent Math Instruction.*

A manila folder makes a sturdy game board,
decorated with pictures from a coloring book.

Dinosaur Race

Math Concepts: number symbols, counting beyond ten, number line.

Players: any number.

Equipment: subitizing cards (page 18), number line racetrack, small plastic dinosaur or other toy for each player.

Set-Up

Draw a straight path on paper or a manila file folder, either horizontal or slanted uphill (so the larger numbers will be higher). Divide the racetrack into twelve to twenty spaces large enough for small toys to rest in. Or glue squares of colored construction paper in a long line on poster board. Number the spaces in order, beginning with one.

Turn the subitizing cards face down and spread them out to form a fishing pond. Do not use dice or regular playing cards. The number of squares moved each turn must be low enough to recognize at a glance, or else counting will distract the player from saying the track numbers in order.

How to Play

Each player should choose a small dinosaur or other toy and place it near the beginning of the racetrack. On your turn, draw a card and move your dinosaur that many spaces, saying each number as you land on it. Cards should be mixed back into the pond after each turn.

This is the most important rule: *when moving their toys, players must say the number in each space.* Repeating the numbers in order focuses the child's attention and helps build number sense, a gut feeling for how numbers work, which is important to future learning.

The first player to reach the end of the path wins the race.

Variations

After children have played the game normally many times, try starting at the end of the path and counting down the number line.

Or use the game board for counting practice. Count pennies or dried beans onto the racetrack spaces, or write numbers on small plastic lids so children can match them to the board.

WHOLE-BODY COUNTING: Draw a Dinosaur Race path outdoors with sidewalk chalk, or use colored painter's tape along a hallway floor. Children can walk or jump along the line, saying the numbers as they go.

History

Counting up and down a number line forms a strong foundation for children's understanding of arithmetic. Dinosaur Race is based on the research of Robert S. Siegler and Geetha B. Ramani, who studied how preschool children responded to a variety of games. Playing a number line game like Dinosaur Race for as little as an hour (in fifteen-minute segments spread out over a couple of weeks) made a dramatic difference in the children's ability to learn and retain arithmetic facts, while similar games played on a round track or on a linear track without numbers produced no measurable change.

Number Train

MATH CONCEPTS: number symbols, numerical order, thinking ahead.
PLAYERS: two or more.
EQUIPMENT: one deck of math cards, or a double deck for more than four players; additional cards to use as train cars.

Set-Up

Give each player four to six miscellaneous cards to serve as the cars of their number trains. Lay these cards face down in a horizontal row, as shown. Shuffle the math card deck and spread it on the table as a fishing pond.

Line up the cars of your train.

How to Play

On your turn, draw one card and play it face up on one of your train cars. The numbers on your train must increase from left to right, but they do not need to be in consecutive order. If you do not have an appropriate blank place for your card, you have two choices:

♦ Mix the new card back into the fishing pond.

♦ Use the new number to replace one of your other cards, and then discard the old one.

Two of the train cars have passengers. Which numbers could you put on the other cars?

The first player to complete a train of numbers that increases from left to right wins the game.

Variation

HOUSE RULE: Decide how strict you will be about the "increases from left to right" rule and repeated numbers. Does "1, 3, 3, 7, 8" count as a valid number train? Or will the player have to keep trying for a card to replace one of the threes?

Childhood Classics

The most profound learning often takes place
silently and invisibly,
*   in between activities*
*   and away from prying eyes.*

It is here that all those pieces of information,
having been shaved from actual experience,
*   are pulled inward to jostle against one another*
*   in various combinations and arrangements*
until gradually,
or sometimes suddenly,
*   a new understanding emerges.*

—HOLLY GRAFF

Quick Tip: Card Holder for Young Hands

LITTLE HANDS OFTEN HAVE TROUBLE holding more than three cards at a time, especially if they need to fan them out and see several cards at once. To help your youngster with this difficult task, make a card holder.

- ♦ Save the plastic lids from two medium-sized plastic tubs such as whipped topping containers.
- ♦ Place the lids top to top, lining up the edges, and staple them together with two or three staples near the center.
- ♦ Let your child decorate the card holder with stickers, if desired.

To use the card holder, slip playing cards between the two lids. This will hold the cards upright, nicely fanned so the child can see them all.

It's easy to make a card holder from plastic lids.

Bango

MATH CONCEPTS: number symbols.
PLAYERS: three or more.
EQUIPMENT: two decks of math cards.

How to Play

With the first deck, deal five (or more) cards to each player except the dealer. Players arrange their cards face up in one or more rows.

Then the dealer shuffles the other deck of math cards and turns up one at a time, reading its value (suit doesn't matter). Any player who has a card with that number turns it face down, but a player may turn only one card down each time.

The first player to turn down all five cards calls "Bango!" and wins the right to deal the next round.

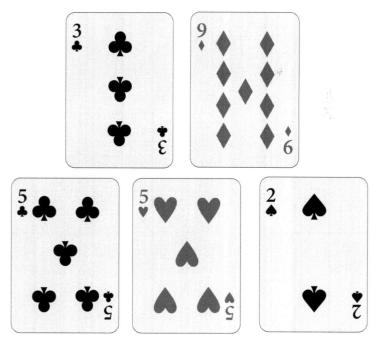

You may arrange your Bango cards face up however you like.

Variation

Bango-Tac-Toe: Deal nine cards to each player, who must arrange them in three rows of three cards each. Or deal sixteen cards, which make four rows of four. The first player to turn down all the cards in a row (vertical, horizontal, or diagonal) wins that round.

History

Also known as Card Bingo, Bango is a simplified version of the traditional five-in-a-row game Bingo. John McLeod offers more Bingo variations at Pagat.com, a wonderful site for learning about card games from around the world.

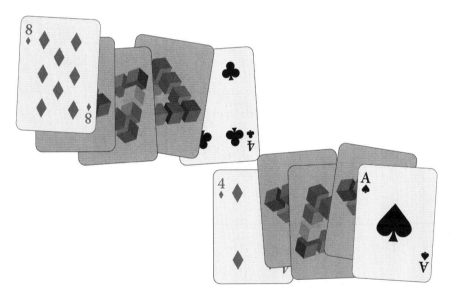

War: If the first cards played have the same value, each player lays three cards face down and then turns up a new card.

War

MATH CONCEPTS: number symbols, less than or greater than.
PLAYERS: two or more.
EQUIPMENT: math cards (one deck per player).

How to Play

Players shuffle their own decks and set them face down on the table or floor. (We usually play on the living room floor.) Then everyone flips their top card face up. The player with the greatest number wins the skirmish, capturing all the cards showing. Each player keeps a pile of prisoner cards.

If there is a tie for greatest card, all the players battle:

♦ Each player lays three cards face down, then a new card face up.

♦ The greatest of these new cards will capture everything played in that turn, including the face-down cards.

Because all players join in, someone who had a low card in the initial skirmish may ultimately win the battle. If there is no greatest card this time, repeat the three-down-one-up battle pattern until someone breaks the tie. The player who wins the battle captures everything.

Then the players go on to the next skirmish, again turning up the top card from each deck.

When the players have fought their way through the entire deck, count the prisoners (or compare the height of the stacks). Whoever has captured the most cards wins the game. Or shuffle the prisoner piles and play on until one player captures all the cards, or until all the other players concede.

Variations

Before play begins, the youngest player picks off part of the deck to reveal a hidden card. This determines whether the goal of the game will be high cards or low. If the exposed card is:

1–5: Lowest card wins each skirmish.

6–10: Highest card wins, as described above.

Two-Digit War: Players turn up two cards and arrange them to form a two-digit number.

Before or After: Players alternate turns, flipping up a card and adding it to the top of a discard pile in the middle of the table. When a player's card is one less or one greater than the previous number, that player captures the whole stack. Then the next player starts a new discard pile.

Crazy Eights

MATH CONCEPTS: identifying and matching card attributes, wild cards, thinking ahead.

PLAYERS: two or more — the more, the merrier.

EQUIPMENT: one complete deck of cards (including face cards), or a double deck for four or more players.

How to Play

Deal eight cards to each player. Place the rest of the deck face down in the middle of the table, and turn the first card face up beside it to start the discard pile. If this card is an eight, shuffle it back into the deck and turn up the new top card.

On your turn, play a card that matches an attribute (suit or number or face card rank) of the most recent discard. Or you can play an eight, which is a wild card and doesn't have to match anything. Whenever you play an eight, you get to name a new suit for the next play.

If you don't have a matching card or an eight to play, you must draw until you find one. When the draw pile is depleted, the dealer shuffles the discard pile (except for the top card) to make a new draw pile.

The first player to run out of cards wins the hand. If you are keeping score, the other players add up the cards they are holding, as follows.

♦ 50 points for each eight

♦ 10 points for each face card

♦ Face value for each number card

Whoever has the lowest score at the end of the party wins the game.

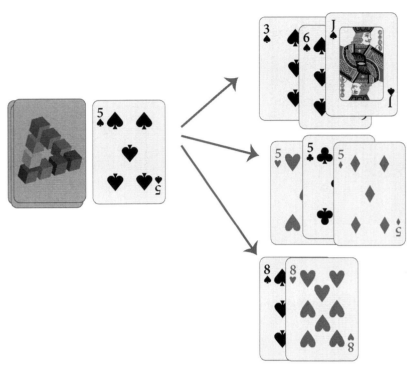

You may play a card that matches the suit or value of the last
card played, or you may play any eight whenever you want.

Variations

The most common variation is that players must announce when they
are playing their next-to-last card. If you forget, you must draw two
penalty cards.

For a shorter game, you're allowed to pass if you can't play after
drawing two cards.

Jokers can serve as additional wild cards, acting like eights.

WILD AND CRAZY EIGHTS: Instead of keeping score, let the winner of
each hand add a new rule, which applies to all future hands until the
party breaks up. Rules must apply equally to all players. For instance:

* ♦ Jacks (or other designated cards) reverse the direction of play.

* ♦ When a two or four is played, the next player must draw that
  many cards and does not get to discard.

- Sevens skip the next player.

- When someone plays a queen, everyone passes their hand to the next player. The person who played the queen may choose whether to pass the cards left or right.

- Play know-it-all style: all players lay their cards face up on the table.

- Draw and skip cards are additive. That is, if you are supposed to draw or be skipped, but you can match the penalty card, then you get to lay down your card. The next player has to draw twice as much, or two players get skipped—unless they can match the penalty card, too.

- All cards must be played left-handed. Players who forget must draw two cards (using their left hand, of course).

- Playing an eight cancels a draw or skip card.

- If you play an ace, you get to give one card from your hand to any other player.

- Prime time: if you play a prime number, you may (or must, if the person making the rule feels mean) play another card.

- Allow runs: if you can match the number (or face card rank) of the card on the discard pile, you may continue to lay down as many additional cards as you wish. Each card in your run must be either the same rank as the card you played immediately before it, or the same suit with a number one up or one down from that previous card.

- Claim jumping: if you have a card that exactly matches the card just played, you may slap it down. Play continues on from your position, skipping the intervening players.

- If you get down to one card, you must recite a (short) poem.

- If you play a king, you may swap hands with the player of your choice.

♦ If you play an eight, you must tell a secret—not a serious secret, but something the other players would not be likely to know.

Instead of making a new rule, the winner of a hand may unmake an earlier one. This option should be used with care, however, since it's the piling on of silly rules that makes the game fun.

Michigan (Boodle): Take the boodle cards from a different deck, not from the deck you are using for the game.

Michigan (Boodle)

MATH CONCEPTS: numerical order, sorting by attribute (card suits), standard rank of playing cards (aces high), thinking ahead.
PLAYERS: three or more, up to as many as fit around your table.
EQUIPMENT: one complete deck of cards (including face cards), plus four boodle cards from a second deck; small prizes to go on the boodle cards. Provide a card holder (page 32) for young children.

Set-Up

Place the boodle cards (also called *pay cards*) face up in the middle of the table: ace of hearts, king of clubs, queen of diamonds, jack of spades. If you'd rather, you can make a game board by folding a piece of paper in half both ways to make four sections where you can write a large J, Q, K, or A and draw the appropriate suit symbol.

Put a prize on each pay card, and add another prize each time a new round is dealt. The boodle prizes might be a coin, a piece of candy, a collectible sticker, or anything else that seems appropriate. Or if you are keeping score with poker chips, then the dealer places two chips on each Boodle card (for a total of eight chips), while the other players put one chip on each of the cards — and you must play enough rounds that everyone takes a turn as dealer.

How to Play

Remind everyone that in this game, aces are the highest cards in each suit. The dealer deals out all the cards one at a time, one hand to each player (including himself) and an extra hand called the *spare*. It doesn't matter if some players end up with one more card than the others have. Players may look at their own cards, but the spare hand is left face down, out of play.

The player to the dealer's left begins by laying down (face up) her lowest card in any suit—it doesn't have to be the lowest in her hand, just in that suit—and saying its name out loud. Whoever has the next higher card in that suit can play, and then the next, with the players putting their own cards face up on the table in front of them as they say the names. The cards are not all mixed together in a discard pile.

Continue until no one can play the next higher card (it may be in the spare hand or have been played earlier) or until someone plays the ace to top out that suit. Then whoever played the last card can start a new run. Like the first player, he may play any suit, but it must be the lowest card he has in that suit.

In the course of play, if you lay down one of the pay cards, you get to claim that boodle prize. Any prize not claimed stays on the boodle, as a bonus for the next hand.

As soon as any player runs out of cards, the play ends. If you are playing for poker chips, then all the other players count their remaining cards and pay that many chips to the player who went out.

Variations

Players must change suit when starting a new run. If the person who played the last card cannot change suit, play would pass to the left until someone can. If none of the players has a different suit, then the hand is done and the remaining boodle prizes are left unclaimed.

PLAY THE SPARE: Before play begins, the dealer may choose to discard his hand and pick up the spare, but he must decide without peeking at the spare cards. If you are playing for chips, then the dealer may instead sell the spare hand to the highest bidder, who must pay the dealer (in chips) and discard her original hand before picking up the spare.

Fan Tan (Sevens)

Math Concepts: sorting by attribute (card suits), counting up, counting down, standard rank of playing cards (aces low).
Players: two or more, best with four to six.
Equipment: one complete deck of cards (including face cards), or a double deck for more than six players. Provide a card holder for young children.

How to Play

Deal out all the cards, even if some players get more than others. The player to the dealer's left begins by playing a seven of any suit. If that player does not have a seven, then the play passes left to the first player who does.

After that, on your turn you may lay down another seven or play on the cards that are already down. If you cannot play, say, "Pass."

Once a seven is played in any suit, the six and the eight of that suit may be played on either side of it, forming the fan. Then the five through ace can go on the six in counting-down order, and the nine through king can go on the eight, counting up. You can arrange these cards to overlap each other so the cards below are visible, or you can square up the stacks so only the top card is seen.

Players do not need to wait for both the six and eight of a suit to be played before they begin building the fan up or down.

The first player to run out of cards wins the game.

If you want to keep score, count the cards remaining in your hand after one player goes out. After everyone has had a turn as dealer, whoever has the lowest total score is the champion.

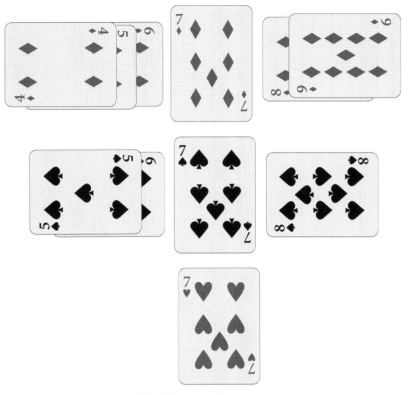

A Fan Tan game in progress.

Variations

In some traditions, play always begins with the seven of diamonds, so whoever has that card goes first.

DOMINO TAN: The player to the dealer's left may lead any card, and then all the suits must start with that number (instead of with seven) and build up and down from there.

FAN TAN TRUMPS: When the dealer gets to the end of the deck and there aren't enough cards to give every player one more, the last few cards are turned face up and may be played by anyone as needed. The suit of the last card becomes the trump suit, and cards of that suit may be played on any of the fans, with the card they replace going on the trumps fan. In this case, the cards must be laid out in overlapping rows, not stacked up, so everyone can see where the trumps have gone.

For instance, if spades are trump, then a nine of spades could be played on the eight of hearts, which would leave the nine of hearts without a home — so it has to go on the spades fan.

Exceptions: The seven of the trump suit starts its own fan, like any other seven, and the last card dealt (the one that named the trump suit) must also be played to the trumps fan when its turn comes.

CRAZY TAN: Deal only seven cards to each player, and set the rest of the deck out as a draw pile. The first player who cannot play must draw one, which he may play if possible. If not, and the next player also cannot play, she must draw two. If neither of those cards will play, and the next player has nothing to play, he must draw three, and so on, each player drawing one more card than the last person. When one of the players is finally able to lay down a card, this resets the draw count back to zero.

In Crazy Tan, players are allowed to lay down a *run* (playing several cards in a row of the same suit on a single turn). Or they may play *parallel cards* (cards of the same rank in different suits, all played in the same turn). Or a player may even lay down parallel runs, if the cards happen to work out that way.

History

Fan Tan may also be called Crazy Sevens. Like any folk game, it is played by a variety of rules around the world. If you search for it on the Internet, you may run into an unrelated Chinese gambling game called Fan Tan, which is similar to Roulette.

The domino train can turn corners and snake around the table as you play.

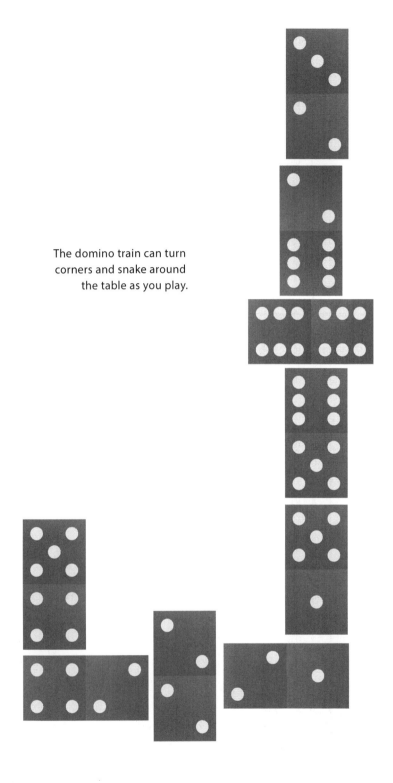

Dominoes

MATH CONCEPTS: subitizing dot patterns, thinking ahead.

PLAYERS: two or more.

EQUIPMENT: one set of double-six or double-nine dominoes, or two sets for five or more players.

Set-Up

Turn all domino tiles (also called *bones*) face down on the table and mix them around. Each player draws several tiles, as follows:

♦ Two players draw seven tiles each.

♦ Three or four players draw five tiles each.

♦ Five or more players use a double set of dominoes and draw five each.

Set your tiles upright on their sides, so the other players cannot see them. These tiles are your hand, and the ones left on the table are called the *wood pile* (also known as the *bone yard*).

How to Play

Whoever has the highest double goes first, placing that tile face up on the table. If no doubles are available, turn everything face down, reshuffle, and draw again.

Play proceeds to the left around the table. Domino tiles are played end-to-end in a long row (the *train*), with only the outer ends available for adding new tiles. On your turn, you may play one of the tiles in your hand to either open end of the train if the dots (called *pips*) on one side of your tile match the tile on that end.

Doubles are placed crosswise to the direction of the train, with the middle of the domino touching its neighboring tiles. Players may not match tiles to the ends of the doubles, however, only to the middle of the other side, continuing the train in whichever direction it was growing.

If you have no tile that will play, draw one tile from the wood pile. If you can play that one, do so. Otherwise, add it to your hand. This marks the end of your turn. If you cannot play from your hand and there are no tiles left to draw, you must pass.

The first player to run out of tiles wins the game (or in Muggins, wins that round). If no player is able to go out, then all players add up the pips on their remaining tiles. The player with the smallest sum wins.

Variations

Domino games vary tremendously around the world, and even from one family to another within the same town. Whenever you play with friends, be sure to agree on the rules before you draw the first tile.

CROSS DOMINOES: Make a double train. After the first double tile is played, the next four tiles must match it. Two of these are placed normally, at the middle of each side of the first tile, and the other two connect to the ends. If players do not have a matching tile, they must pass. After the four matching tiles have made a cross shape, play continues normally, except in four directions instead of two.

MUGGINS: Play as for Cross Dominoes, but keep score as you go along. At the end of each turn, the player adds up the pips showing on the live tiles at all four ends of the train, including both halves of any exposed doubles. If these make a multiple of five, the player adds that number to his or her score. At the end of each round, players add up the pips remaining in their hands, round to the nearest five, and subtract those points from their total so far. The first player to reach 200 points (or some other agreed-upon total) wins the game.

FIVES AND THREES: Play as for Muggins, but score all multiples of three or five.

History (and a Puzzle)

Domino-like tile games seem to have originated in China, and they came to Europe through the great trading cities of Venice and Naples. Some game historians claim the European game was invented independently, because European domino sets are different from Chinese sets in several ways. (For instance, Chinese tiles come in suits, like a set of playing cards.) Dominoes spread across France and reached England in the late eighteenth century, where the game became a favorite pastime in British pubs.

Encourage your children to examine a set of domino tiles and describe what they notice. For example, every possible combination (double-0, 0|1, 0|2, etc.) is a single tile, but there are no duplicates: 0|1 is the same tile as 1|0.

Ask them, "If you bought a set of dominoes at a garage sale, how could you tell whether any of the tiles were missing? Can you figure out how many tiles there should be?"[†]

[†] *Spoiler: To find the answer, make a systematic list, and be careful not to count any of the combinations twice. A double-six set should have twenty-eight tiles, and a double-nine set will have fifty-five. A new set from the store may contain extra blank tiles, which can be decorated with paint or white nail polish to replace lost pieces.*

Number Bonds

A hundred years ago,
researchers in logic discovered
    that virtually all of the concepts
        used by working mathematicians
could be reduced to one of two extremely basic operations,
    namely, the operation of counting
        or the operation of grouping objects into sets.

Most people are able to perform both of these operations
before they enter kindergarten.

It is surprising, therefore,
that schools have managed to make mathematics
    a mystery to so many students.

—John Mighton

Quick Tip: Play with Number Bonds

A NUMBER BOND IS A mental picture of the relationship between a number and the parts that combine to make it. With young children, use pennies, popsicle sticks, or whatever you have on hand to make physical piles that can be pulled apart and pushed back together, and then pulled apart another way.

My youngest daughter and I spent read-aloud time sprawled on the master bed. When the story was finished, she wanted to play math. I dropped six blocks in the middle of the bedspread.

"How many blocks do we have here?" I asked.

She counted carefully. "1, 2, 3, 4, 5, 6."

"I'm going to move these blocks over to make a new pile," I said. I pushed two of the blocks to one side. "How many blocks did I move?"

She did not have to count those. "Two."

"And how many are left?"

"1, 2, 3, 4."

"And if I push them back together…" I did so. "Two and four are how many in all?"

"1, 2, 3, 4, 5, 6."

"Two and four are six. You are so good at counting! Now, this time I'm going to move three blocks over here." I moved three blocks to the side. "How many are left?"

Again, she did not need to count. "Three."

I pushed the blocks back together. "And three and three are how many?"

I could see her lips move as she counted silently. She looked up and smiled. "Six."

"That's right. Three and three are six. What will happen if I move just one block over?" I did so. "How many are left?"

She started to speak, then stopped with a puzzled look on her face. She bent over to hide the blocks with her hand so I could not see her count. "1, 2, 3, 4, 5."

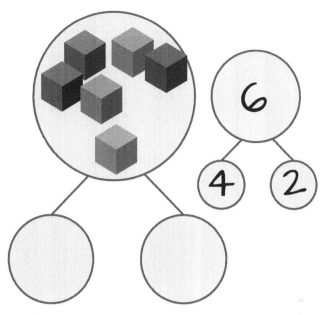

Number bond diagram: The six blocks can be pulled into two smaller parts — for instance, four blocks and two blocks — and then pushed back together to show the whole amount.

"Oh, you're tricky!" I said. "Five blocks. And if I put them back together, one and five are how many?"

I pushed the blocks together again. She looked at the pile. "Six."

"One and five are six. Now you try it. What piles will you make?"

She pushed all six blocks to the side. She gave me an uncertain half-smile, as if she thought that might not be allowed.

"Okay," I said. "You moved six blocks. How many are left?"

She looked at the empty spot. "Zero."

"That's right. Zero blocks. And if you put the piles back together, six and zero make how many?"

She answered triumphantly, "Six!"

We played this short sort-of-game for several days, taking turns to split up piles of various sizes. I didn't want her to memorize specific number relationships, but to realize she could take any number apart in many different ways.

If we parents push our kids to memorize number facts too early, we short-circuit the child's learning process because once children know an answer, they dismiss it from their minds. But if we can keep them in the thinking-about-it stage, they will build a logical foundation for understanding all numbers.

Number bonds are an elementary version of the mathematical concept of partitions — counting all the different ways a whole number can be broken into whole-number parts. For more information, check out James Tanton's online lesson "Partition Numbers: An Accessible Overview."[†]

---

† *Remember, all the blogs, websites, and other resources I mention are listed in the appendix "Quotes and Reference Links" on page 170*

Odd One Out

MATH CONCEPTS: simple addition, number bonds for five.
PLAYERS: two or more.
EQUIPMENT: one deck of math cards, or a double deck for three or more players, and one face card.

How to Play

Remove all numbers greater than five from the deck, and add a single face card. For young hands, be sure to provide a card holder (page 32).

Shuffle well and deal out all the cards. It does not matter if some players get one more card than the others. All players remove from their hands any fives and any pairs of cards that add up to five. Lay these cards face up on the table, so everyone can see that the discarded pairs match.

On your turn, you may ask any other player for a card. That player must fan out his or her cards as much as possible and hold them so you cannot see the numbers. Then you may choose any card you wish. If the card you take will combine with one of the cards in your hand to make a sum of five, discard the pair. Otherwise, place the card in your hand.

When all the cards are paired and set aside, the player left holding the face card loses the game.

Variations

At our house, we take from the player to our right, so each player first gets a card and then gives one to the next player.

You can play with other number bonds, collecting pairs that add up to eight, or to ten. Whichever number you choose, remove all higher numbers from the deck.

History

Many traditional children's games can be adapted to play with number bonds. This is a mathy version of Old Maid.

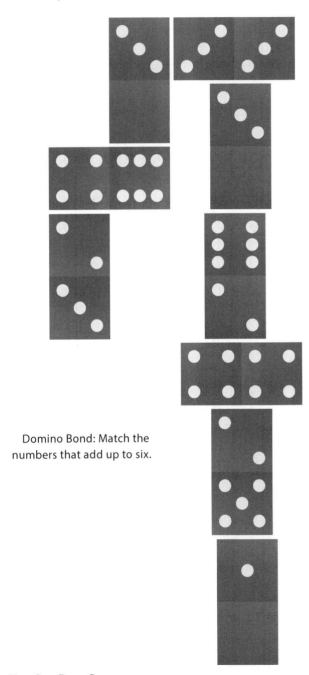

Domino Bond: Match the
numbers that add up to six.

Domino Bond

MATH CONCEPTS: addition, number bonds for six.
PLAYERS: two or more.
EQUIPMENT: one set of double-six dominoes.

Set-Up

Turn all domino tiles face down on the table and mix them around to make the wood pile. Each player draws several tiles, as follows:

♦ Two players draw seven tiles each.

♦ Three or four players draw five tiles each.

♦ Five or more players use a double set of dominoes and draw five each.

Set your tiles upright on their sides, so the other players cannot see them.

How to Play

Whoever has the highest double goes first, placing that tile face up on the table. If no doubles are available, turn everything face down, reshuffle, and draw again.

On your turn, you may play one of the domino tiles in your hand to either open end of the train, if the pips on one side of your tile and on the end of the train add up to six. For instance, a two can be played next to a four, or a blank next to a six.

If you have nothing that will play, you may draw one tile from the wood pile. If you can play that one, do so. Otherwise, add it to your hand. This marks the end of your turn. If you cannot play from your hand and there are no tiles left to draw, you must pass.

The first player to run out of tiles wins the game.

Variations

Try playing any of the domino variations on page 48 with a number bond matching rule.

FIVES DOMINOES: For very young players, remove all tiles with sixes on them. Play by matching tiles that add up to five.

TENS DOMINOES: Use a double-nine set of dominoes, removing all the tiles with blanks. Begin play with the double nine or the largest available double tile. Match numbers that add together to make ten.

Nine Cards: Claim the ten and the pairs of cards that add up to ten. Do not take longer sums, like 5 + 2 + 3.

Nine Cards

MATH CONCEPTS: addition, number bonds for ten.
PLAYERS: two or more.
EQUIPMENT: one deck of math cards.

How to Play

The first player shuffles the deck and then turns up the top nine cards, placing them face up in a 3 × 3 array: three rows with three cards in each row. The player captures (removes and keeps) any tens and any pairs of cards that sum to ten, then passes the deck to the next player.

Each player in turn deals out enough cards to fill in the empty spots in the array—or, if there are no empty spots to fill, the player covers all nine cards with new ones. Then capture any tens and any pairs that make ten, and pass the deck on.

The game ends when the deck is gone or when there are not enough cards left to fill in the holes in the array. Whoever has collected the most cards wins the game.

Variation

CONCENTRATION (MEMORY): Lay all the cards out face down on the table in a single layer with no overlaps. On your turn, flip up two cards. If you find a ten or a number bond, take it. If not, leave the cards showing long enough that all the players can see what they are. Then turn them face down before the next player's turn.

History

Tens Concentration has always been one of my favorite math games. The face-up Nine Cards version comes from Constance Kamii's *Young Children Continue to Reinvent Arithmetic.*

Tens Go Fish

Math Concepts: addition, number bonds for ten.
Players: two or more.
Equipment: one deck of math cards.

How to Play

Deal seven cards to each player, or five cards if you have four or more players. Put the remaining cards face down in the center of the table and spread them out to make a roughly circular fishing pond. Players look at their own hands and set aside any tens and any pairs that add up to ten, making their "fish basket" score piles.

On your turn, you may ask one other player, "Do you have a _____?" The blank is for a number that will pair with one of the cards in your hand to make a sum of ten. For instance, if you have a three, you might ask, "Do you have a seven?" If there are more than two players, the request must be addressed to a specific person. You may ask, "George, do you have a six?" but it is illegal to say, "Does anyone have a six?"

If George has the card you want, he must give it to you. If not, he says, "Go Fish." Then you draw any card you wish from the fishing pond. If you draw a ten, add it to your fish basket and draw again. If you draw a card that makes a pair of ten with any card in your hand, add that pair to your fish basket. Otherwise, add the card to your hand.

The game is over when one player runs out of cards. The other players throw their remaining cards into the fishing pond. (Those fish were too small to keep.) Then all players count the cards in their fish basket pile. Whoever caught the most fish wins the game.

Variation

If you get the card you asked for, either from the other player or the pond, you get a free turn and may ask any player for another card.

Shut the Box

MATH CONCEPTS: addition, number bonds up to nine.
PLAYERS: two or more.
EQUIPMENT: paper and pencil or pen for each player, two six-sided dice.

Set-Up

Players make their own game boards by writing the numbers from one to nine on a piece of blank paper. These may be decorated and laminated for frequent play, in which case each player will need an erasable marker or nine tokens for covering the numbers.

Or make a game board with flaps from the free download *Number Game Printables Pack.*[†] Decorate as desired.

How to Play

On your turn, roll the dice and add the numbers together. Cross out or cover one or more numbers that add up to make that sum. For instance, if you roll a six and a four, you could cover the 8 and 2, or the 6 and 4, or the 7 and 2 and 1, or any other combination that makes a sum of ten. If you cannot cover the full amount of your roll, you don't get to cover anything. Pass the dice to the next player.

If all the higher numbers are already covered, a player may choose to roll only one die. The first player to cross out or cover all the numbers wins the game.

Variations

Traditionally, each player takes a single, long turn. You keep playing until you roll a sum you can't cover, and then you add up the uncovered

---

† *TabletopAcademy.net/Free-Printables*

numbers to make your score. Pass the box to the next player. Whoever gets the lowest score wins the game.

Children may also enjoy playing Shut the Box as a solitaire game.

PLUS OR MINUS: Players may choose to cover either the sum or difference of the numbers on their dice. Subtraction offers more options near the end of the game, when there are only a few numbers left to cover.

PHONE NUMBER COVER-UP: Make a game board with the digits of your phone number (or any other number you want your child to memorize). Decorate as desired and laminate for repeated play.

THE LONG GAME: (For two players.) The first player tries to cover all the numbers on the game board, going until he rolls a number he can't play. If that last roll was a double, he gets to roll once more, and if he can cover that free roll, he keeps going until he's stumped again. Then the second player takes the same game board, but she tries to uncover

Cut only this far.

Fold game board here.

Print on card stock or regular paper.

- Cut away excess margins.
- Cut along each solid line above, from the outer edge of the paper to the dotted line.
- Fold along the dashed center line.
- Put two or three staples in the uncut area to hold the game board together.

Begin playing with all flaps folded open.

1 2 3 4 5 6 7 8 9

You don't need a game board for
Shut the Box, but it's fun to have one.

Or use cards as your "game board": start with all the cards in a suit face up. How many can you turn down?

all the numbers that the first player covered. She keeps rolling until she gets a number she can't uncover (taking a free turn if that roll was a double), then passes the board back to the first player. Whoever succeeds in covering or uncovering all the numbers wins the game.

History

Shut the Box is a traditional English pub game, also known as Canoga, which may have been played as early as the twelfth century in Normandy. The "box" is a wooden tray with a row of numbers one to nine along the top length, each with a cover that can either slide or swing to hide the number. As a gambling game, each player would ante an agreed amount into a pool, which would be awarded to the winner.

Phone Number Cover-Up was created by first grade teacher Sharon McGlohn and shared by Alice P. Wakefield in *Early Childhood Number Games: Teachers Reinvent Math Instruction.*

Bigger Numbers

People have this notion
that math is about getting a right answer,
and the testing really emphasizes that notion.
And that's such a bad way to approach math
because it makes it scary.

When you look at little kids,
they pose their own questions.
They say, "Ooooh, what's bigger than a million?"
And they think about things their own way.

At school,
the teacher poses the questions,
*   and the students answer their questions.*
Schooling is not a natural environment for learning.

— Sue VanHattum

Linear Number Line

Logarithmic Number Line

Mental Number Line

Activity: Pondering Large Numbers

HUMAN INTUITION SERVES US WELL for the numbers we deal with from day to day, but it has a hard time with numbers outside our experience. Try this simple yet fascinating activity:

♦ Draw a line on paper, with dots or bars at each end.

♦ Label the left end "0" and the right end "100."

♦ Ask your child to point to where ten should go on the line. (Don't mark it.)

♦ Where would eighteen be?

♦ How about eighty-five? Forty-seven? Three?

Children can visualize the small numbers that they commonly work with, but they must rely on vague notions of "big, bigger, biggest" to deal with large numbers.

Our intuitive number sense seems to work on an almost-logarithmic scale with the small numbers spread out, and the bigger the numbers get, the closer they crowd together. For very young children, one hundred seems almost the same as infinity.

Our mental number line starts like a linear scale, but as the numbers get larger, they squeeze closer together.

Teenagers and adults respond in a similar way if you let the number line range up to a million or more. I challenged my high school math students with a version of this puzzle. If you're curious about their response, see my blog post "Pondering Large Numbers."

Twenty-One

MATH CONCEPTS: counting to twenty-one, thinking ahead.
PLAYERS: two or more.
EQUIPMENT: none.

How to Play

The first player says "one" or "one, two" or "one, two, three." Each player then counts in turn, increasing the total by one, two, or three numbers. Whoever is forced to say "twenty-one" loses the game.

If there are more than two players, the player who says "twenty-one" drops out of the game. The next person in the rotation starts a new round by counting from one, and play continues. The loser of each round drops out, until only one player (the winner) remains.

Variations

Choose a different "poison" number. Or allow a different number of counts per turn. Or count down from your chosen number, and the person who says "zero" loses the game.

TWISTER: The first player rolls a six-sided die and says that number. Then each player in turn tips the die, turning a number that had been on the side up to the top, and then adds that number to the current total. The player who exactly reaches twenty-one, or who forces the next player to go over, wins the game.

THE CALENDAR GAME: The first player says any date in January. Then each player in turn increases either the month or the day (but never both at once) and says a new date later in the year. Whoever says December 31 loses the game.

History

Twenty-One is a variation of Nim, one of the oldest and most flexible math games in the world. Nim is traditionally played as a *misère game,* which means that the player who makes the final move loses. But feel free to tweak the strategy by making the final move the winner instead.

Jim Pardun shared the Calendar Game in a comment on Dan Meyer's "Tiny Math Games" blog post.

Fifty Sticker Race

MATH CONCEPTS: counting to fifty, how to read a hundred chart.
PLAYERS: any number.
EQUIPMENT: one six-sided die, one game board for each player, sheet or roll of small stickers (fifty per player), scissors.

Set-Up

This is a variation of Dinosaur Race for older students. By cutting the correct number of stickers from a roll or sheet, you separate the counting step from the number line move, so players can read the numbers out loud without the mental dissonance of having to count spaces.

Each player will need a copy of the game board from the *Number Game Printables Pack* and a roll or sheet of stickers. Each player may have a separate pair of scissors, or a shared pair may be passed around the table with the die.

The fifty chart is like a number line cut up and laid in rows. Arrows guide the child from line to line.

How to Play

On your turn, roll the die and cut that many stickers from your sticker sheet. Beginning with the number one, put a sticker on each square, saying aloud each number as you cover it. When you reach the end of a row, follow the arrow down to the next line of numbers.

The first player to cover all fifty squares wins the race. Other players may continue to take turns with the die until they fill their own charts.

What's My Number?

MATH CONCEPTS: numbers to one hundred, greater than or less than, strategic guessing.
PLAYERS: only two.
EQUIPMENT: forty small tokens, printed hundred chart.

How to Play

Each player starts with twenty tokens. One player chooses a secret number from one to one hundred. The other player pays a token for each guess by placing it on a number on the hundred chart. The first player signals thumb-up if the secret number is greater than the guess or thumb-down if it is less.

91	92	93	94	95	96	97	98	99	100
81	82	83	84	85	86	87	88	89	90
71	72	73	74	75	76	77	78	79	80
61	62	63	64	65	66	67	68	69	70
51	52	53	54	55	56	57	58	59	60
41	42	43	44	45	46	47	48	49	50
31	32	33	34	35	36	37	38	39	40
21	22	23	24	25	26	27	28	29	30
11	12	13	14	15	16	17	18	19	20
1	2	3	4	5	6	7	8	9	10

Many children find the bottoms-up hundred chart more logical than the traditional top-down version. It makes intuitive sense to have the numbers get larger as they climb up the page. The *Number Game Printables Pack* includes both styles.

When the number is correct, the player who had the secret collects all the tokens from the chart. Then the players trade roles. Play as many complete rounds as desired or until one player runs out of tokens.

Variation

Play orally for an easy travel game. To keep score, count how many guesses it takes to find the other player's number. This is a good place for finger counting, since children can hold up a finger for each guess without distracting their minds from the hunt for the secret number.

History

This game is a variation on the traditional guessing game Twenty Questions. I read a version online or in a book somewhere that used nickels as the tokens, so each player would start with one dollar's worth of coins and pay a nickel for every guess. But I neglected to jot down the reference, and I haven't been able to find it since. If you know where The Nickel Game comes from, I'd love to hear from you.

Two-Digit Number Train

MATH CONCEPTS: place value, numerical order, thinking ahead.
PLAYERS: two or more.
EQUIPMENT: one deck of math cards plus queens, pencil and paper or whiteboard and markers.

Set-Up

Decide how long your number trains will be: five to ten spaces. Players draw their own number trains on paper or on a whiteboard. A train may be any shape (a simple row of boxes, stair steps, a caterpillar of ovals with legs, or a chain of flowers with open centers for writing in) and may curl around the page in any direction, but it must have a clear beginning and end. Each space must have enough room to write a two-digit number.

If you draw the trains on paper, you can laminate these drawings or slip them into sheet protectors for repeated play. But if you make a new drawing each time, then the Number Train game can grow longer and express the children's personalities as their artistic skills develop.

How to Play

Remove the tens from your deck of cards and replace them with queens to represent the number zero — or leave in the tens, but count them as zeros. Shuffle well, and then spread the cards face down as a fishing pond.

On your turn, draw two cards and arrange them to make a two-digit number. You may use a zero (queen) as the tens digit, if you wish, which makes the equivalent of a one-digit number: Q6 = "06" = 6. Write your number into any blank space in your train, making sure that the numbers increase from the beginning of your number train to the end, and then mix the cards back into the pond. Be careful: once

Would you make the number 27, or is 72 a better choice?

written, your number may not be erased.

If you cannot make a number that fits, discard. You have to wait until your next turn to try again. The first player to complete an ordered train of increasing numbers wins the game.

Variations

Draw three cards at a time to make a three-digit number train. Or include the tens, which count as two digits by themselves — and which means that the size of the numbers in your train will vary, depending on which cards you draw.

Do you want to give children a way to undo mistaken moves? Allow players to erase a number from their train. This uses up the whole turn, so the player does not draw any cards.

Snugglenumber

Math Concepts: place value, probability, thinking ahead.
Players: any number.
Equipment: one deck of math cards, pens or pencils, blank paper or game boards.

Set-Up

You can print game boards or write the numbers 0, 5, 10, 25, 50, 100 down the center of your paper. These are the *snugglenumbers* (target numbers). Next to each number, draw as many blanks as there are digits in the target number. These blanks are where you do your snuggling. The printable sheet has two columns of blanks, which can be used for two separate games. Or two players may share one game board, each using one of the columns.

Remove the tens from your deck of cards and replace them with queens to represent the number zero — or leave in the tens, but count them as zeros. Shuffle the deck and place it in the center of the table where everyone can reach.

The Snugglenumber game board is included in the *Number Game Printables Pack,* but it's easy to make your own.

How to Play

On your turn, flip one card face up beside the deck. Each player must write that number on one of their blanks, trying to create numbers in each row that are as close to the snugglenumbers as possible. The next player waits until everyone has filled a blank before turning up the next card.

Once you have written a digit, it cannot be moved. But the printable game board includes a trash can symbol, so once in each game you can decide to throw away a card, writing its number value in the can instead of on a blank.

When all the blanks are filled in, players compare their numbers. Whoever has the snuggliest number in each row gets a point. In the case of a tie—either the players made the same number, or they made two numbers that are equally close to the target—both players earn a point. Whoever wins the most points wins the game.

A Sample Game

Sven challenged Olaf to a game of Snugglenumber. Olaf drew first, turning up an ace. Both players wrote a one on their game board. Olaf put his by the zero. Since one is very close to zero, he thought he had a good chance of winning that row. Sven wrote his one in the hundreds place.

Then Sven turned up a four, so both players found a place for that digit. Sven wrote his four next to the five—only one point away, a likely winner. Olaf put his four in the tens place next to the fifty, figuring a large number was bound to come along for the ones place.

Olaf's turn to draw, and he got an eight. He wrote it next to the four, making forty-eight and snuggling very close to the fifty. Sven put the eight in the twenty-five row, hoping to draw a two later in the game.

Sven turned up a six, and the players wrote it in. Then Olaf turned up a queen, which stands for a zero. Sven pounced on the chance to

		Olaf				Sven		
		1	0	0				
			5	4				
		_	0	10	_	_		
		_	6	25	_	8		
		4	8	50	_	_		
		0	_	_	100	1	0	6

Snugglenumber game in progress. If the next
card is a six, where would you put it?

score on the zero row. Olaf put his zero in the hundreds place, hoping
to draw nines later. Then Sven turned up another zero...

Variations

For older students, the players subtract the numbers they made from
the snugglenumbers—or vice versa, depending on which is bigger—and then add up all these differences. The player with the smallest total difference wins.

HORSESHOES: Deal eleven cards to each player. Arrange your cards in
the snuggle-chart pattern so that the number on each line comes as
close to the target number as you can get it. Score according to horse-
shoe rules:

♦ 3 points for each *ringer*, or exact hit on the target.

♦ 1 point for each number that is six or less away from the
  target.

- If none of the players land in the scoring range for one of the target numbers, then score 1 point for the number closest to that target.

For a quick game, whoever scores the most points wins. Or follow horseshoes tradition and keep going until one player gets 21 points (40 points for a championship game). In traditional horseshoes, you have to win by at least 2 points over your closest opponent's score.

History

I first saw place value games on the late-1980s PBS *Square One Television* series, which had a faux game show routine called "But Who's Counting?" Math teacher Anna Weltman posted this version at her blog Recipes for π.

"The game of Snugglenumber has taken my school by storm," Weltman writes. "Kids from third grade to tenth-grade Algebra 2 beg to play it. It involves the seemingly mundane arithmetic concept of place value. And yet, everyone loves it…

"Oh, and did I mention that when you say Snugglenumber you *must* scrunch up your nose, smile adorably, and coo, 'Snug-gle-num-ber'?"

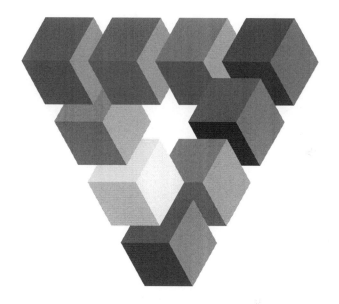

Addition &
Subtraction Games

Tens and Teens

Schools spend a lot of time working with young children to get these facts memorized, but many children aren't ready for that task yet. They'll count on their fingers, and may be reprimanded for it.

What happens when a person becomes embarrassed about counting on their fingers? If they still want to think, they'll hide it. That's the better option.

The worse option that way too many students choose? They start guessing. When math becomes too incomprehensible, or not living up to someone else's expectations becomes too painful, many students give up on math, and then they just guess.

We count on our fingers as part of a thinking process. Perhaps the thing I want to figure can be memorized. But if I haven't memorized it yet myself, the most efficient way to figure it will likely involve fingers.

— Sue VanHattum

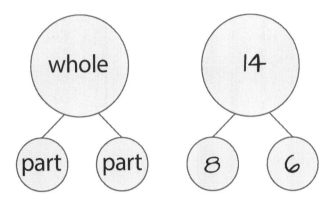

Number bond diagrams help children see that a number can be broken into parts in many different ways. Or the parts can be put back together to make the whole thing.

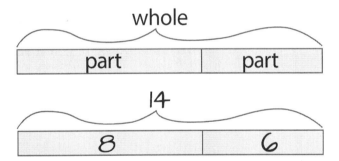

Quick Tip: Number Bonds Build Understanding

A NUMBER BOND IS A mental picture of the relationship between a number and the parts that combine to make it. Number bonds can be shown on paper using circles or bar model diagrams. Imagine the circles as a pile of blocks or other small toys. We can pull the pile apart to make smaller piles that we can push back together or slide apart in different ways. Think of the bar diagram as all the toys lined up in a row.

Either drawing incorporates two foundational concepts about the way numbers work.

A whole thing is made up of parts.

If you know both of the parts, you can add to find the whole. If you know the whole and one part, you subtract the part you know to find the other part.

Subtraction is a mirror image of addition.

To subtract means to figure out how much more you would have to add to the part you know in order to get the whole thing.

Math textbooks often try to communicate these concepts using four-fact families. A four-fact family looks like this:

$$6 + 8 = 14$$
$$8 + 6 = 14$$
$$14 - 6 = 8$$
$$14 - 8 = 6$$

The idea of the four-fact family is for students to realize that once they know one of the facts in the family, they know all of them. Many students never see the connection, however, and think of these equations as separate little bits of abstract information, all of which have to be memorized. This can overload their minds and make them give up on math. Number bonds connect with the student's understanding at a deeper, intuitive level, showing all four relationships in a single picture.

Our goal at this age is not for our children to memorize a series of abstract number facts like "6 + 1 = 7, 6 + 2 = 8, 6 + 3…" but for them to develop confidence in working with numbers. If we stress fact memorization too early, we short-circuit their learning process. Once children "know" an answer, they don't bother to think about it—but it is in the "thinking about it" stage that they build a logical foundation for understanding all numbers.

Number bonds are an elementary version of the mathematical concept of partitions—counting all the different ways a whole number can be broken into whole-number parts. For more information, check out James Tanton's online lesson "Partition Numbers: An Accessible Overview."

Tens Concentration

MATH CONCEPTS: addition, number bonds for ten, visual/spatial memory.
PLAYERS: any number.
EQUIPMENT: one deck of math cards.

How to Play

Shuffle the cards and lay them all face down on the table, spread out in a single layer. The cards may be placed in an orderly array (five rows of eight cards each) or arranged in a haphazard cloud, as long as no card covers any other card.

On your turn, flip two cards face up. If one of the cards is a ten, you may take it at once and flip another card face up. If the pair of face-up

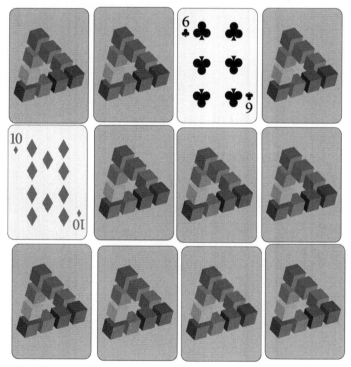

Tens Concentration: When you turn up a ten, take it. Then turn over another card to see if you can match a four with the six.

cards add together to make ten, you get to take the pair. If they do not make ten, leave them showing for a few seconds so all players can see what they are, then turn the cards face down and let the next player take a turn.

Keep the cards you capture in a score pile. When all the cards are claimed, whichever player has collected the most is the winner.

Variations

HOUSE RULE: How will you avoid the frustrating cycle where one player uncovers a new card and sees how to make a pair, but the other player grabs it before the first player's turn can come back around? At our house, if you find a pair, you get a free turn and can flip over two more cards—which means every player exposes new cards that the next player can use. Free turns expire when there are ten or fewer cards left on the table, to keep one lucky player from claiming all the last pairs.

MIXED GROUPS: When playing with a wide range of ages, let the younger players flip three cards per turn and keep any two that add up to ten.

History

Tens Concentration is my favorite ice-breaker game for math club meetings because the game is quick to learn and easy to play in large groups. It is also a game that older children and adults can enjoy as much as the beginning students do. More than once, when my teenage daughter walked through the room where the younger children were playing, she asked to join in the game.

Shut the Box

MATH CONCEPTS: addition, number bonds up to twelve.

PLAYERS: two or more.

EQUIPMENT: paper and pencil or pen for each player, three six-sided dice.

Set-Up

Players make their own game boards by writing the numbers from one to twelve on a piece of blank paper. These may be decorated and laminated for frequent play, in which case each player will need an erasable marker or twelve tokens for covering the numbers.

Or make a game board with flaps from the *Number Game Printables Pack*.[†] Decorate as desired.

How to Play

On your turn, roll the dice and add the numbers together. Cross out or cover one or more numbers that add up to make that sum. For instance, if you roll a two, a three, and a five, you could cover the 10, or the 6 and 4, or the 7 and 2 and 1, or any other combination that makes a sum of ten. If you cannot cover the full amount of your roll, you don't get to cover anything. Pass the dice to the next player.

After you cover the 10, 11, and 12, roll only two dice on each turn—and if you get down to just the small numbers, you may choose to roll only one die. The first player to cross out or cover all the numbers wins the game.

Variations

Traditionally, each player takes a single, long turn. You keep playing until you roll a sum you can't cover, and then you add up the uncovered

---

† *TabletopAcademy.net/Free-Printables*

numbers to make your score. Pass the box to the next player. Whoever gets the lowest score wins the game.

Children may also enjoy playing Shut the Box as a solitaire game.

PLUS OR MINUS: Players may choose to cover either the sum or difference of the numbers on their dice. Subtraction offers more options near the end of the game, when there are only a few numbers left to cover.

PHONE NUMBER COVER-UP: Make a game board with the digits of your phone number (or any other number you want your child to memorize). Decorate as desired and laminate for repeated play.

THE LONG GAME: (For two players.) The first player tries to cover all the numbers on the game board, going until he rolls a number he can't play. If that last roll was a double, he gets to roll once more, and if he can cover that free roll, he keeps going until he's stumped again. Then the second player takes the same game board, but she tries to uncover

Cut only this far.

Fold game board here.
Print on card stock or regular paper.
- Cut away excess margins.
- Cut along each solid line above, from the outer edge of the paper to the dotted line.
- Fold along the dashed center line.
- Put two or three staples in the uncut area to hold the game board together.

Begin playing with all flaps folded open.

1 2 3 4 5 6 7 8 9 10 11 12

You don't need a game board for
Shut the Box, but it's fun to have one.

Or use cards as your "game board": start with all the cards
in a suit face up. How many can you turn down?

all the numbers that the first player covered. She keeps rolling until
she gets a number she can't uncover (taking a free turn if that roll was
a double), then passes the board back to the first player. Whoever succeeds in covering or uncovering all the numbers wins the game.

History

Shut the Box is a traditional English pub game, also known as Canoga,
which may have been played as early as the twelfth century in Normandy. The "box" is a wooden tray with a row of numbers one to nine
along the top length, each with a cover that can either slide or swing
to hide the number. As a gambling game, each player would ante an
agreed amount into a pool, which would be awarded to the winner.

Phone Number Cover-Up was created by first grade teacher
Sharon McGlohn and shared by Alice P. Wakefield in *Early Childhood
Number Games: Teachers Reinvent Math Instruction*.

Addition War

MATH CONCEPTS: counting, less than or greater than, addition, subtraction.

PLAYERS: two or more.

EQUIPMENT: math cards (one deck per player).

How to Play

Players shuffle their own decks and place them face down on the table or floor. (We usually play on the living room floor.) Then everyone turns their top two cards face up and adds the numbers together. The player with the greatest sum wins the skirmish, capturing all the cards showing. Each player keeps a pile of prisoners.

If there is a tie for greatest sum, push all the cards into a center pile. Then the players go on to the next skirmish, again turning up the top two cards from each of their decks. The winner of that skirmish takes the center pile as well. If there is no winner this time, repeat until someone wins a battle and captures the whole pile.

When the players have fought their way through the entire deck, count the prisoners (or compare the height of the stacks). Whoever has captured the most cards wins the game. Or shuffle the prisoner piles and play on until one player captures all the cards, or until all the other players concede.

Variations

Before play begins, the youngest player picks off part of the deck to reveal a hidden card. This determines whether the goal of the game will be high numbers or low. If the exposed card is:

1–5: Lowest sum wins each skirmish.

6–10: Highest sum wins, as described above.

SUBTRACTION WAR: Players turn up two cards and subtract the smaller number from the larger. This time, the greatest difference wins the skirmish.

MATH WAR TRUMPS: Players alternate choosing "trump" for the math card battles. After the cards are turned up, the player whose turn it is gets to say which operation (addition or subtraction) to do.

ADVANCED ADDITION WAR: Turn up three (or four) cards for each skirmish and add them together. Greatest sum wins. Players may end up with one or two cards at the end of their decks. Draw enough cards from your prisoner pile to finish the last skirmish.

ADVANCED SUBTRACTION WAR: Remove the tens from the deck. Turn up three cards. Make two of them into a two-digit number, and then subtract the third. Suppose you turn up a three, a four, and a five. Should you arrange them as 34 – 5 or 45 – 3 or 35 – 4 or…?

History

This classic children's card game adapts easily for practicing a variety of number facts. A math card deck contains forty cards, so a single game of Addition War lets a child practice twenty problems. And if your children are like mine, they will rarely want to stop after one time through the deck.

My students usually need extra practice on the hard-to-remember calculations. To give a greater challenge to older children, I make each player a double deck of math cards, but I remove the aces, twos, and tens. This gives each player a fifty-six-card deck full of the toughest problems. For even more of a challenge, use the face cards as additional numbers: jack = eleven, queen = twelve, king = thirteen.

Fifteen

MATH CONCEPTS: addition to fifteen, thinking ahead.
PLAYERS: only two.
EQUIPMENT: one deck of math cards.

How to Play

Separate the deck of math cards into the four suits—hearts, spades, diamonds, and clubs. Set aside the tens from each suit, and put the suits face down on the table in four stacks.

The dealer chooses one stack and lays the cards face up on the table. The cards do not have to be in numerical order. Then beginning with the non-dealer, take turns picking up a card. The first player to get three cards that add up to fifteen wins the hand and captures all the cards from that suit.

The losing player gets to choose whether to deal or pick first for the next suit.

If neither player can find three cards that make fifteen, the hand is a draw. Lay down the cards and play that suit again—and this time, use the ten card, too. Whoever dealt the draw gets first pick on the replay.

After all four suits have been claimed, whoever collected the most cards wins. If the players are tied when the deck is gone, play a run-off round. Whoever lost the last hand can choose to deal or pick. It doesn't matter which suit the dealer puts out. The player who wins this round is the champion.

Variation

HOUSE RULE: How will you handle mistakes? If a player has three winning cards but does not notice it, should the other player point it out? At our house, the other player may continue trying to make a set.

Then the first player to announce having three cards that add up to fifteen wins the hand.

History

Recreational math hobbyist Martin Gardner described this game and several related games in *Mathematical Carnival*. If you can't find that book, pick up any of the books based on Gardner's long-running *Scientific American* "Mathematical Games" column. You won't be disappointed.

The players have taken all the cards. Did either of them get fifteen? Or is this hand a draw?

It's easy to draw your own number line, or you can print a
game board from the *Number Game Printables Pack*.

$$5 + 7 = 12$$
$$12 - 8 = 4$$
$$4 + 16 = 20$$

A sample game of Strike It Out. I've written equations to show
each turn's play, but players may explain their moves orally.

Strike It Out

MATH CONCEPTS: addition, subtraction, thinking ahead.
PLAYERS: only two.
EQUIPMENT: pencil or pen, blank paper.

How to Play

Draw a number line and label the numbers 0–20. The first player strikes two numbers (draws a line through them) and circles their sum, saying the equation. Once a number has been struck out, it cannot be used in any future turn.

Then the second player must strike out the number the first player circled and one unused number, and then circle either their sum or their difference. Be sure to say your equation out loud, so the other player can check your mental math.

The first player has to add, but after the first turn you may choose to add or to subtract. Continue to take turns striking two numbers (one of which must be the answer from the last turn) and circling their sum or difference.

Eventually, of course, the numbers will run out. Whoever makes the last legal move wins the game.

History

Strike It Out is from the Nrich website, which is part of the Millennium Mathematics Project, a math education initiative from the University of Cambridge. The Nrich site is full of mathematical activities and resources for teachers and school-age students. Browse and enjoy.[†]

---

† *Remember, all the blogs, websites, and other resources I mention are listed in the appendix ""Quotes and Reference Links" on page 170.*

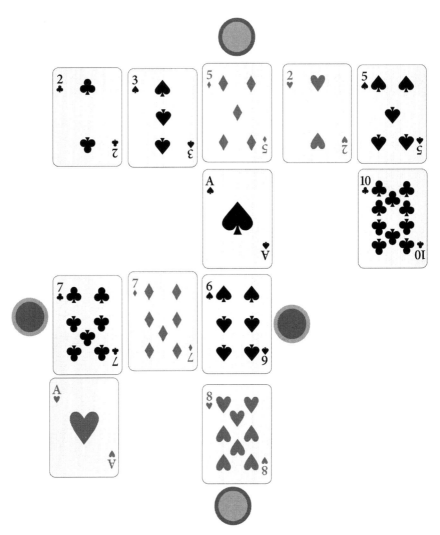

Cross-Twenties game in progress. What numbers
would let you finish another row of twenty?.

Cross-Twenties

MATH CONCEPTS: addition to twenty, thinking ahead.
PLAYERS: two or more.
EQUIPMENT: two decks of math cards, six tokens per player.

How to Play

Shuffle the two decks of cards together. Deal five cards to each player, and give each player six tokens. Turn one card face up to start the game. Place the remaining stack of cards face down as a draw pile.

On your turn, place one card face up on the table so that it lines up with the side, top, or bottom edge of a card already played. Then draw a replacement so you always have five cards in your hand.

The cards on the table will form a crossword-style pattern, but no row or column of the pattern is allowed to go over a sum of twenty. If your card makes a row or column (or both) add up to exactly twenty, put one of your tokens at each end to mark that sum as completed.

The first player to make three twenties, and thus run out of tokens, wins the game.

History

Constance Kamii called this game Twenty-Twenty in her book *Young Children Continue to Reinvent Arithmetic*. You can also play with a double-nine set of dominoes, as Kamii does in her third-grade book.

Numbers to One Hundred

Mathematical competence involves a blend of skills, knowledge, procedures, understanding, reasoning, and application.

But too often, instruction focuses on skills, knowledge, and performance—that is, what students know and are able to do. Thus, students learn to use routine methods, leading to superficial understanding.

We don't spend enough time on reasoning and on deep understanding—that is, why and how mathematics works. For deep understanding, the what, the why, and the how must be well connected.

— David A. Sousa

Quick Tip: Mental Math Part 1

BY LEARNING TO THINK IN number bonds, students grow comfortable with taking numbers apart and putting them back together in their heads. They are able to understand and use a variety of methods to figure out a new problem.

As children progress to larger numbers, keep this playful attitude. How might your children figure out a calculation like 27 + 45 without pencil and paper?

Highest Place Value First, with Funny Numbers

Working with numbers in the order we say them makes intuitive sense to me, so this is probably how I would do it with my kids. We add the tens first, then the ones.

$$20 + 40 = 60$$
$$7 + 5 = 12$$
$$\text{Answer} = \text{"sixty-twelve"}$$

Then, after we chuckle at the funny number, we convert it to the equivalent and more familiar seventy-two.

Move the Pieces

We imagine each number as a pile of toys, blocks, stones, or whatever, and we can move the pieces from one pile to another without changing the total amount. This strategy is often called "friendly numbers," since our goal is to create numbers we can work with easily. Twenty-seven is close to thirty, so you can imagine moving three of the pieces over from the forty-five pile.

$$27 + 45$$
$$= 30 + 42 = 72$$

Or you could move five from the first pile, if you'd rather.

$$27 + 45$$
$$= 22 + 50$$
$$= 72$$

We do this more often with small numbers, when my kids are first learning the addition and subtraction facts within twenty. Then I tend to get out of the habit of thinking this way, maybe because I can't actually visualize the piles, but the trick works for any size of number.

Of course, this method is easiest when the number of pieces moved is small, so you may want to reserve it for problems with some-thingty-eight or somethingty-nine in them.

$$29 + 45$$
$$= 30 + 44$$
$$= 74$$

[Continued on page 116.]

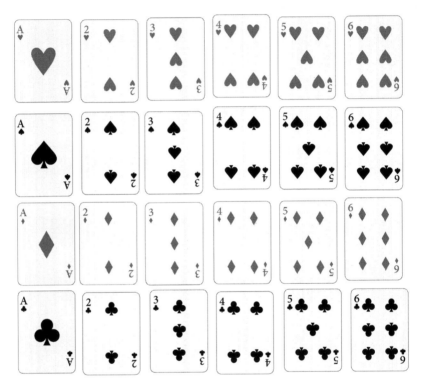

Ready to start a game of Thirty-One.

Thirty-One

MATH CONCEPTS: addition to thirty-one, thinking ahead.
PLAYERS: best for two.
EQUIPMENT: one deck of math cards.

How to Play

Lay out the ace to six of each suit in a row, face up and not overlapping, one suit above another. You will have one column of four aces, a column of four twos, and so on — six columns in all.

The first player flips a card upside down and says its number value. Players alternate, each time turning down one card, mentally adding its value to the running total, and saying the new sum out loud. The player who exactly reaches thirty-one, or who forces the next player to go over that sum, wins the game.

Variation

For a shorter game, use only the ace to four of each suit. Play to a target sum of twenty-two.

History (and a Puzzle)

Thirty-One comes from British mathematician Henry Dudeney's classic book, *The Canterbury Puzzles*. According to Dudeney, "This is a game that used to be (and may be to this day, for aught I know) a favourite means of swindling employed by card-sharpers at racecourses and in railway carriages."

Dudeney challenges his readers to find a rule by which a player can always win: "Now, the question is, in order to win, should you turn down the first card, or courteously request your opponent to do so? And how should you conduct your play?"

91	92	93	94	95	96	97	98	99	100
81	82	83	84	85	86	87	88	89	90
71	72	73	74	75	76	77	78	79	80
61	62	63	64	65	66	67	68	69	70
51	52	53	54	55	56	57	58	59	60
41	42	43	44	45	46	47	48	49	50
31	32	33	34	35	36	37	38	39	40
21	22	23	24	25	26	27	28	29	30
11	12	13	14	15	16	17	18	19	20
1	2	3	4	5	6	7	8	9	10

Many children find the bottoms-up hundred chart more logical than the traditional top-down version. It makes intuitive sense to have the numbers get larger as they climb up the page. The *Number Game Printables Pack* includes both styles.

Push the Penny

MATH CONCEPTS: addition to one hundred, thinking ahead.
PLAYERS: two or more.
EQUIPMENT: one deck of math cards, a hundred chart, and a penny or other small token.

How to Play

Deal three cards per player and set the rest of the deck face down as a draw pile. Print your choice of hundred chart from the *Number Game Printables Pack.*[†] Place the chart in the middle of the table, with the penny on the first square.

On your turn, lay one card from your hand face up on the discard pile. Move the penny forward that many squares, and then draw to replenish your hand.

If adding the number on your card would move the penny past one hundred, then you must subtract your number and move backward instead. Whoever pushes the penny to one hundred by exact count wins the game.

Variations

Play two cards from your hand and choose whether you want to add or subtract the numbers to find out how far the penny moves.

Or start at one hundred and push the penny down to number one.

History

My math club students have enjoyed playing a variety of count-to-one-hundred games. This version is a modification of the 99 Game from Julie Reulbach's collection "Math Games for Classrooms."

[†] *TabletopAcademy.net/Free-Printables*

Dollar Nim

MATH CONCEPTS: subtraction within one hundred, value of coins, thinking ahead.

PLAYERS: best for two.

EQUIPMENT: none.

How to Play

This is a mental math game, designed to be played in the car. Start by imagining a pile of money equal to $1, or 100 cents. On your turn, "remove" any coin you like—quarter, dime, nickel, or penny. Say which coin you are taking and the new value of the pile. The player who claims the last coin wins the game.

Variations

Allow half-dollar coins, if you wish, but no dollar coins—unless you are trying to demonstrate what mathematicians mean by a "trivial" problem.

HUNDRED CHART NIM: If your children have trouble doing the subtraction mentally, you may use a penny or other small token to keep track of your value on a printed hundred chart. Whoever wins gets to keep the penny.

MAKING CHANGE: Play with real coins. Each player starts with one quarter, two dimes, three nickels, and four pennies. Or pick different coins, as long as everyone starts with the same collection. On your turn, discard one of your coins to a pile on the table. If there are any smaller coins in the pile, you may take back change up to one cent less than the value of the coin you put in. The last player who has money wins the game.

ALIEN MONEY: Imagine an alien civilization. What sorts of coins would they use? Perhaps the creatures have three fingers on each hand, so their coins are all multiples of three. Or maybe the alien society loves math so much that they put mathematicians on their coins instead of political leaders, and their coins are based on prime numbers. What is the value of an alien dollar? How would your aliens play Dollar Nim?

History

One of the oldest and most flexible strategy games in the world, Nim began with players taking one or more stones away from one or more piles. It's usually played as a *misère* game, which means that the player who takes the last stone loses.

Nadine Block invented Dollar Nim on the way home from a camping trip, thus earning her official title: Mother of Twins and Creator of Math Games on Long Car Rides. I read about the game on her husband Patrick Vennebush's blog, Math Jokes 4 Mathy Folks, named after his fun book, which Block helped edit.

Making Change is based on James Ernest's game Fight, now renamed Pennywise. I found it at John Golden's Math Hombre blog.

Countdown

MATH CONCEPTS: subtraction within one hundred, thinking ahead.
PLAYERS: best for two.
EQUIPMENT: a hundred chart, penny or other token to mark your place.

How to Play

Start with the penny on one hundred (or ninety-nine, if you prefer the 0–99 chart). The first player subtracts any amount from one to ninety-nine (ninety-eight on the alternate chart) and moves the penny to the new number.

On each succeeding turn, players subtract any amount from one up to twice as much as the previous move—but keep in mind that your opponent will then be able to subtract up to twice as much as you do.

The player who gets to zero wins the game.

Variation

THE CALENDAR GAME: The first player says any date in January. Then each player in turn increases either the month or the day (but never both at once) and says a new date later in the year. Whoever says December 31 loses the game.

History

Countdown can also be called Fibonacci Nim. It was originally described by M. J. Whinihan and is included in the book *Winning Ways for Your Mathematical Plays, Volume 4*, by Elwyn R. Berlekamp, John H. Conway, and Richard K. Guy. I discovered it in an online lesson by Geoff Patterson.

Jim Pardun shared the Calendar Game in a comment on Dan Meyer's "Tiny Math Games" blog post.

Euclid's Game

MATH CONCEPTS: subtraction within one hundred, number patterns.
PLAYERS: best for two.
EQUIPMENT: blank paper and pen or pencil, or printed hundred chart and highlighter or translucent Bingo chips to mark numbers.

How to Play

Allow the youngest player choice of moving first or second; in future games, allow the loser of the last game to choose. The first player picks a number from one to one hundred and writes that number on the paper (or marks that square on the hundred chart). The second player writes or marks any other number, *except* that the second number may not be exactly double or exactly half the first choice.

On each succeeding turn, players subtract any two marked numbers to find and write a difference that has not yet been taken. Play alternates until no more numbers can be made. The player who marks the last number wins the game.

For Advanced Students

Play several rounds of Euclid's Game on printed hundred charts. Circle the original pair of numbers in each game, and use a highlighter to mark all the numbers you use. Then study your collection of finished game boards.

- ◆ Do you notice any patterns in the numbers marked on each game board?
- ◆ Can you explain why some games have few numbers marked while others have many?
- ◆ If you knew the first two numbers, would you be able to predict how many squares would be marked in the end?

History

A. J. Cole and A. J. T. Davie invented the Euclid game and analyzed it for an article in *The Mathematical Gazette*, December 1969. I learned the game from Alexander Bogomolny's amazing website Cut the Knot, which I encourage you to explore.

The Snugglenumber game board is included in the *Number Game Printables Pack,* but it's easy to make your own.

Snugglenumber

Math Concepts: place value, probability, thinking ahead.
Players: any number.
Equipment: one deck of math cards, pens or pencils, blank paper or game boards.

Set-Up

You can print game boards or write the numbers 0, 5, 10, 25, 50, 100 down the center of your paper. These are the *snugglenumbers* (target numbers). Next to each number, draw as many blanks as there are digits in the target number. These blanks are where you do your snuggling. The printable sheet has two columns of blanks, which can be used for two separate games. Or two players may share one game board, each using one of the columns.

Remove the tens from your deck of cards and replace them with queens to represent the number zero—or leave in the tens, but count them as zeros. Shuffle the deck and place it in the center of the table where all can reach.

How to Play

On your turn, flip one card face up beside the deck. Each player must write that number on one of their blanks, trying to create numbers in each row that are as close to the snugglenumbers as possible. The next player waits until everyone has filled a blank before turning up the next card.

Once you have written a digit, it cannot be moved. But the printable game board includes a trash can symbol, so once in each game you can decide to throw away a card, writing its number value in the can instead of on a blank.

When all the blanks are filled in, players compare their numbers.

Whoever has the snuggliest number in each row gets a point. In the case of a tie—either the players made the same number, or they made two numbers that are equally close to the target—both players earn a point. Whoever wins the most points wins the game.

A Sample Game

Sven challenged Olaf to a game of Snugglenumber. Olaf drew first, turning up an ace. Both players wrote a one on their game board. Olaf put his by the zero. Since one is very close to zero, he thought he had a good chance to win that row. Sven wrote his one in the hundreds place.

Then Sven turned up a four, so both players found a place for that digit. Sven wrote his four next to the five—only one point away, a likely winner. Olaf put his four in the tens place next to the fifty, figuring a large number was bound to come along for the ones place.

Olaf's turn to draw, and he got an eight. He wrote it next to the four, making forty-eight and snuggling very close to the fifty. Sven put the eight in the twenty-five row, hoping to draw a two later in the game.

Sven turned up a six, and the players wrote it in. Then Olaf turned up a queen, which stands for a zero. Sven pounced on the chance to score on the zero row. Olaf put his zero in the hundreds place, hoping to draw nines later.

Then Sven turned up another zero…

Variations

For older students, the players subtract the numbers they made from the snugglenumbers—or vice versa, depending on which is bigger—and then add up all these differences. The player with the smallest total difference wins.

HORSESHOES: Deal eleven cards to each player. Arrange your cards in the snuggle-chart pattern so that the number on each line comes as

Olaf				Sven	
1	0	0			
	5	4			
	0	10			
	6	25		8	
4	8	50			
0		100	1	0	6

Snugglenumber game in progress. If the next
card is a six, where would you put it?

close to the target number as you can get it. Score according to horse-shoe rules:

- ◆ 3 points for each *ringer*, or exact hit on the target.
- ◆ 1 point for each number that is six or less away from the target.
- ◆ If none of the players land in the scoring range for one of the target numbers, then score 1 point for the number closest to that target.

For a quick game, whoever scores the most points wins. Or follow horseshoes tradition and keep going until one player gets 21 points (40 points for a championship game). In traditional horseshoes, you have to win by at least 2 points over your closest opponent's score.

History

I first saw place value games on the late-1980s PBS *Square One Television* series, which had a faux game show routine called "But Who's Counting?" Math teacher Anna Weltman posted this version at her blog Recipes for π.

"The game of Snugglenumber has taken my school by storm," Weltman writes. "Kids from third grade to tenth-grade Algebra 2 beg to play it. It involves the seemingly mundane arithmetic concept of place value. And yet, everyone loves it…

"Oh, and did I mention that when you say Snugglenumber you *must* scrunch up your nose, smile adorably, and coo, 'Snug-gle-num-ber'?"

Mixed Operations

I do hate sums. There is no greater mistake than to call arithmetic an exact science. There are Permutations and Aberrations discernible to minds entirely noble like mine; subtle variations which ordinary accountants fail to discover; hidden laws of Number which it requires a mind like mine to perceive.

For instance, if you add a sum from the bottom up, and then again from the top down, the result is always different.

Again if you multiply a number by another number before you have had your tea, and then again after, the product will be different. It is also remarkable that the Post-tea product is more likely to agree with other people's calculations than the Pre-tea result.

Try the experiment, and if you do not find it as I say, you are a mere sciolist, a poor mechanical thinker, and not gifted as I am, with subtle perceptions.[†]

—MARIA PRICE LA TOUCHE

---

† *A sciolist is someone who freely offers opinions and advice, despite having only superficial knowledge of the topic at hand.*

Quick Tip: Mental Math Part 2

IN THE LAST CHAPTER (PAGE 100), we covered two ways to figure out a sum like 27 + 45 mentally. Here are two more tricks your children may find helpful.

If Only, If Only…

This is another "friendly number" strategy. We look for a simpler (but related) calculation that we would rather do, and then we adjust the answer. I will often pose the simpler problem as a question: "If only the problem was 30 + 45, that would be easier. Could you do that one?"

After the student solves that calculation, we decide how we need to adjust it to get back to the original problem. In this case, we added too much, so we will have to take the extra bits back off.

"We were only supposed to add twenty-seven, and we added thirty. How many extra is that? How can we fix our answer?"

$$27 + 45$$
$$= 30 + 45 - 3$$
$$= 75 - 3 = 72$$

Add in Chunks

This is much easier to do mentally than to explain on paper. Again, we start with the big place value, in this case the tens. We break one of the numbers apart (it doesn't matter which one) into whatever chunks seem easiest to keep track of as we work:

$$27 + 45$$
$$= 27 + 40 + 5$$
$$= 67 + 5$$
$$= 67 + 3 + 2$$
$$= 70 + 2 = 72$$

As in all the other methods, we would not write out the interme-diate steps, just keep track of them mentally. The kids might point to the numbers and say the steps aloud, but more often they just mutter under their breath. Sometimes they stare at the problem or look off into space as if they don't know what to do, but if I wait patiently, I find that their minds are working behind those blank eyes, and the answer comes out.

If I get too impatient and offer a hint, my children usually let me know: "Mom, be quiet. I'm thinking!" But by that point, I've broken their concentration, so they have to start the problem over. No wonder they get mad at me for it.

Target Ten

Math Concepts: addition, subtraction, multistep calculation.
Players: any number.
Equipment: one deck of math cards, pencils and paper, timer (optional).

How to Play

Deal five cards to each player, face up on the table. Players list all the ways they can think of combining any two or more of their own cards to make a total of ten. Numbers may be added or subtracted, but each card may be used only once in each calculation. For instance, you could not use the expression 5 + 5 unless you were dealt two fives.

If you were dealt 2, 3, 5, 7, and 10, you might make the following combinations:

$$10$$
$$3 + 7$$
$$10 + 5 - 3 - 2$$
$$7 + 5 - 2$$
etc.

This is not a racing game, but you may want to set a reasonable time limit of perhaps two to ten minutes, depending on the age and patience level of the players.

Each valid expression scores 1 point per card used. The player with the highest score is the winner.

Variations

To eliminate the element of chance, deal five cards face up in the middle of the table. All players use these cards to see how many ways they can make ten.

How many different ways can you make ten by adding and subtracting?

HOUSE RULE: Will you count 3 + 7 as different from 7 + 3? If a player is dealt two threes and a seven, does that count as two different ways to make 3 + 7? I do not count these as separate combinations, but you may if you wish.

FOR YOUNGER STUDENTS: Make this a cooperative game by working together to find all the possible ways to make ten in each player's hand. Offer hints to help your students find the multistep combinations. "How many more does seven need to make ten? Can you find a way to combine two of your cards to make three? Here's a five and a two…"

FOR OLDER STUDENTS: Allow multiplication and division. This will give your children more possible ways to make ten, but it will also give them an unfair advantage if they are playing against a younger child.

TARGET X: Before dealing to the players, turn up one card in the center of the table to be the target number for this hand.

History

Target Ten is based on "Five Cards Make 10" from Peggy Kaye's delightful book, *Games for Math*. Kaye describes many other games and activities for exploring math with preschool and early elementary children. If you have not read her book, be sure to look for it the next time you visit your local library.

Make and Take

Math Concepts: addition, subtraction, multistep calculation.
Players: only two.
Equipment: one deck of math cards.

How to Play

Deal each player five cards. Turn the remainder of the deck face down as a draw pile. Players do not take turns, but play at the same time:

- ♦ Choose one of your cards as a challenge to your opponent. Hold it out face down. When both of you are ready, turn the challenge cards face up.

- ♦ Try to combine two or more of the cards left in your hand by adding or subtracting them to make the number on your opponent's challenge card. If you can make it, lay down those cards and say the calculation.

- ♦ If you make your opponent's card, you can take it for your score stash. If you can't make the challenge card, it goes on the discard pile.

Then pick up the cards you used to make the challenge number, and return them to your hand. Draw one more to bring your hand back to five for the next turn. If necessary, shuffle the discards to replenish the draw pile.

The first player to capture ten cards wins the game. If both players get ten on the same turn, then add up the numbers on your captured cards, and the player with the highest total wins.

Variations

For a shorter game, play to five or seven captures. For a tougher game deal four cards to each player, so each will have only three cards left for making the challenge number.

BONUSES: If you made the challenge number using all the cards in your hand, you can also capture the smallest of those cards as a bonus. You can also claim a bonus if you used cards that are all the same suit—and if your cards all matched the suit of the challenge card, you can capture the smallest two of them. Bonuses are additive, so if you used all the cards in your hand and they all matched the challenge card's suit, you could claim three bonus cards.

NONMATCHING SETS: If there is no way to combine your cards and make the challenge number, you may still claim it by showing your hand to prove it's impossible. But if your opponent can demonstrate a way to use your cards to make the number, then he or she gets to capture the card.

CATCH UP: If you can't make your opponent's challenge card on one turn, leave it on the table (don't discard). On the next turn, you may either make the new challenge card by itself or try to claim both of them by making their sum.

History

This game was created by Grand Valley State University mathematics associate professor John Golden and math/physics teacher Nicholas Smith and published on Golden's fantastic Math Hombre blog.

Tiguous

MATH CONCEPTS: addition, subtraction, multistep calculation.
PLAYERS: two or more.
EQUIPMENT: game board, three six-sided dice, pencil or marker(s), scratch paper for keeping score.

Set-Up

You can print the Tiguous game board from the *Number Game Printables Pack,* download the Contig, Jr. game from Terry Kawas's Math-Wire website, or have your children make their own game board.

If students make their own board, they can arrange the numbers however they like:

- ◆ Draw a 6 × 6 grid of squares, each big enough for a two-digit number.

- ◆ The first player writes the number one in any square. The next chooses a square for the number two. Players take turns writing the numbers 1–18 anywhere they wish, one number per square.

- ◆ After eighteen, the next player goes back to one, and the turns continue until the board is full.

How to Play

On your turn, roll all three dice. If any die falls off the table or lands at a slant, all three dice must be rolled again. Do not touch the dice with your hands after they are rolled, though you may use a pencil or marker to scoot them next to each other.

Add or subtract these three numbers in a two-step equation that equals the number in any unmarked square on the game board. Think of as many possible combinations as you can, in order to choose the

Which square would you mark?

highest-scoring square. Mark your answer on the game board with a large X. At the same time, say out loud how you calculated the number.

You score 1 point for the square you marked, plus 1 point for each already-marked square that is touching (*contiguous* to) any side or corner of your number's square. The maximum score for any turn is 9 points. If all the numbers you can make have already been marked, you score a zero—but if anyone else can find a valid calculation using your dice, that player may challenge you, mark the square, and "steal" those points.

If another player thinks you made an arithmetic mistake, that person may challenge your answer before the next player rolls the dice. If your answer was wrong, the challenger takes the points you would have won, and you score zero. If your calculation is correct, you get one bonus point for having withstood the challenge.

Play until each player has had ten turns, or five turns each for three or more players. Whoever has the highest total score wins the game.

Variations

The most common variation I have seen is not to score a point for the marked square. Just score 1 point for each contiguous square that was previously marked, which makes the maximum possible score per turn only 8 points. I strongly prefer the scoring system above, which awards at least 1 point for any valid calculation.

TIGUOUS-TAC-TOE: Two players mark numbers with X and O, and the first player to get three squares in a row wins. Rows may be vertical, horizontal, or diagonal. For a longer game, try to get four or five in a row.

MULTIPLAYER EXTENDED GAME: Keep playing until almost all the numbers are marked. Any player who gets a zero three turns in a row drops out of the game. When the last player gets a third strike, the game is over. There is no bonus for the last player, other than the extra turn(s).

TOURNAMENT RULES: Two players per game board. Set a timer, giving each player only thirty seconds for each turn. Think fast! If you do not mark a square within the thirty seconds, your score is zero for that turn. Scores of zero may not be challenged in tournament play, but opponents may challenge arithmetic errors. After each player has ten turns, add up the players' scores for that round. Then trade partners, get a new game board, and play another round. After three rounds, award 1st, 2nd, and 3rd place ribbons to the top scorers in each age group/ grade level.

History

Tiguous is a simplified version of F. W. Broadbent's game Contig, which is played on a larger board and allows the use of multiplication and division. I took the name from an even simpler version by Constance Kamii.

For as long as I can remember, our local homeschool group has held a series of Contig practices every spring. Then we host a "school" tournament, and the top two players in each grade level proceed to a regional tournament against other public and private school teams.

Bowling

MATH CONCEPTS: addition, subtraction, multistep calculation, column addition (for final score).

PLAYERS: any number.

EQUIPMENT: one deck of math cards, game board, ten tokens for covering numbers, pencil or pen, and (optional) scratch paper for adding up the scores.

Set-Up

You can print the bowling game board and score sheet from the *Number Game Printables Pack,* or draw your own game board and use the printable score sheets from the Apollo's Templates website.

How to Play

Place the deck face down where all players can reach. When it's your turn, roll your bowling ball by flipping up three cards. On your game board, cover the pins you knock down:

- ♦ The numbers on your cards.

- ♦ Any numbers you can make by adding or subtracting two cards.

- ♦ Any numbers you can make by adding and subtracting with all three of the cards. Each card may be used only once in each calculation.

For example, if you roll a two, four, and ace, you can cover those numbers and also $3 = 4 - 1$, $7 = 1 + 2 + 4$, and more.

If you cover all the numbers, you rolled a *strike,* and that's the end of your turn. If you don't cover all the numbers, discard those cards and turn up three more for your next ball. Can you cover the remain-

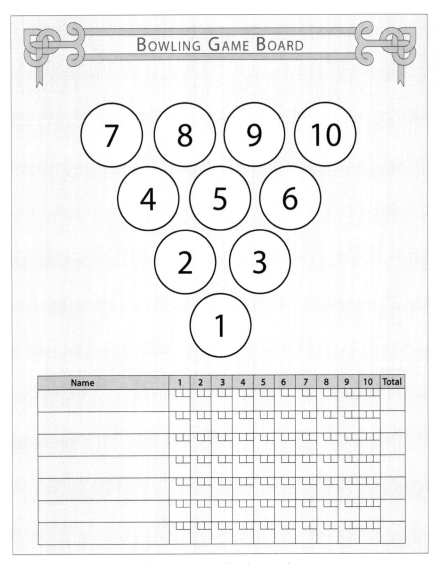

Bowling game board and score sheet.

ing numbers now? If so, that's a *spare*. Your score for each turn is how many numbers you cover, with special rules for strikes and spares as explained below.

After you roll two balls, the next player takes a turn. Keep going until each player has ten turns. If the draw pile runs out of cards, reshuffle the discards to replenish it.

How to Use the Score Sheet

The rules for keeping score in bowling seem confusing until you've played a few games. Each larger square box on the score sheet is called a *frame* and represents your score for one turn. The two (or three) smaller square boxes are for keeping track of each time you roll your ball.

One complete game of bowling consists of ten turns, with a maximum score of 300 points. You might think that with ten numbers to cover in each turn, the most you could score would be 100 points, but strikes and spares get bonuses.

For each turn, write down how many numbers you covered with your first ball in the first small box, or if you got a strike, mark an X there. If you threw a second ball, mark down how many more numbers you covered in the second small box, or if you got a spare, write a slash (/). If you did not get a strike or spare, add the numbers you wrote down and put that total score at the bottom of the frame.

A spare earns one bonus ball, and a strike earns two, which means you can't finish scoring your frame yet. On your next turn, the balls you throw will count not only for their own frame but also as bonus points on your strike or spare. After you've thrown your next ball (or two balls, for a strike), add ten for the strike or spare plus the value of the bonus(es) and write in that total at the bottom of the unfinished frame.

Notice that the bonus balls get counted twice, once as part of the strike or spare and once for their own frame. And if you throw three strikes in a row, the third one will be counted three times:

- As the second bonus throw in the first strike frame.
- As the first bonus throw on the second strike.
- And finally as part of its own frame, along with its own bonus balls.

When you get to the last frame, you will see three small boxes. That's because any players lucky enough to throw a strike or a spare still get their bonus balls. If you don't get a strike or spare, ignore that third little box.

Finally, add up all the points from all ten frames to make your total score for the game.

Logic and Probability

One of my objectives was to teach the kids to identify an ill-defined problem and turn it into a "good" problem.

The first problem I gave them was: "Two kittens together weigh less than their cat mom. Do three kittens weigh more than their mom?"

This problem caused a lot of discussion. Some kids said more, some said less. When one boy said they were equal, the kids realized that something was wrong, but they were not sure what. I asked them whether the kittens were well fed or not.

Eventually, our discussion of all types of cats and kittens led us to conclude that some problems are ill-defined and cannot be solved the way they are stated. We also analyzed what basic information was missing from the problem statement.

Finally, we wrapped it up by asking for all the ill-defined problems they could come up with, which was hilarious.

—JULIA BRODSKY

Activity: The Messed-Up Labels

FOR ELEMENTARY STUDENTS, LOGIC MEANS reasoning, debating, and explaining how they figured something out. Here's a classic puzzle to stretch your children's thinking skills. It takes a bit of preparation on your part, but it's worth the effort. You will need:

- ◆ Three shoe boxes or other opaque containers
- ◆ Two different types of items small enough to fit inside
- ◆ Three blank index cards for making label signs

Set-Up

Put some of the first type of item in the first box, some of the second type of item in the second box, and a mixture of both types in the third box. Fold the index cards horizontally to make a stand-up sign, and then label them to match the boxes. Use a small piece of tape to stick the signs on the boxes—*but be sure to put each sign on a wrong box.* For instance, the Lego label might go on the mixed box, and the Mixed label on the dinosaur box, and so on.

How to Play

Now you are ready to challenge your children.

> *"I sorted the toys and put them in boxes, but then I got all confused. Can you help me straighten them out?*
>
> *"I know that one box has only Legos, and one box has only dinosaurs, and one box has some Legos and some dinosaurs mixed together.*
>
> *"But my signs are all on the wrong boxes."*

Of course, your kids aren't allowed to lift the lids to see what is inside the boxes. That wouldn't be a puzzle! Instead:

Shoe boxes labeled and ready for puzzling.

♦ They pick one of the boxes.

♦ You pull out one toy from inside.

♦ Set the toy on top of that box.

Each time the children pick a box, you pull out another toy. When they think they have it figured out, they can move the labels to whichever box seems right to them. They can discuss and switch things around until they are satisfied.

Finally, let them open the boxes to see if they got it right.

After that, your children can put the toys back into the boxes and mess up the labels for you to untangle. How many clues do you need to guarantee your answer is correct?[†]

---

† Spoiler: An alert reasoner can solve this puzzle in one step by choosing the Mixed box. Since the Mixed label has to be wrong, whatever toy is pulled out identifies the sign that belongs on that box. Set the Mixed sign aside and put the correct one in place.

That will leave you with one unlabeled box and one that still has its wrong sign. The box with the wrong label must really be the mixed toys, so switch those signs.

Now you have one box without a label and one sign without a box, which means they must go together. Puzzle solved.

Dice Miner

MATH CONCEPTS: number line, addition to twelve, probability with dice.
PLAYERS: any number.
EQUIPMENT: two six-sided dice, eleven tokens per player, paper and pencil.

How to Play

Draw a number line across the length of your paper and mark the numbers 2–12. Arrange your eleven tokens on these numbers, spread out evenly, piled up on just one number, or shared out however you like. These are the treasures you'll be mining for.

On your turn, dig in your treasure mine by rolling the dice. and adding the two numbers If you have any tokens on that sum, you hit pay dirt! Take one token off your number. The first player to remove all eleven tokens wins the game.

Variations

The challenging part of this game is the set-up. Talk to your kids about their strategies. How did they decide where to place their tokens?

HORSE RACE: Write the numbers 2–12 down the left side of your paper, and draw four boxes in a row next to each number. Each box represents one-fourth of the way around the race track. Place one token (horse) on each number. On your turn, roll the dice and add the two numbers. Move that horse ahead one space. Which horse do you think will win the race?

History

Marilyn Burns calls this the Two Dice Sum Game in her book *About Teaching Mathematics*. I had forgotten about the game until I read Joshua Greene's blog post "Dice Mining."

The Ten Cards

MATH CONCEPTS: logic, strategic thinking.
PLAYERS: only two.
EQUIPMENT: one deck of math cards.

How to Play

The dealer lays out ten cards, face up, in a row on the table. It doesn't matter which numbers are showing or whether they are in numerical order, just that they are face up. The other player turns one of these cards face down.

On each succeeding turn, players may choose to turn down one or two cards, but they can only turn down two cards if they are directly next to each other. The player who turns down the last of the ten cards wins that hand and collects the ten cards as a prize.

Then the person who played first the last time has a turn as dealer, turning up ten new cards in a row. Play continues as above until both players have dealt twice and all the cards are claimed.

Whoever collects the most cards wins the game. If both players have won two hands, then they may play a run-off hand. Each of them turns up five cards from their previous winnings, and whoever lost the last hand may choose whether to take the first move or pass. The winner of this hand is declared the champion.

It's your turn. Which card(s) will you turn down?.

History

The Ten Cards was featured in *536 Puzzles and Curious Problems* by Henry Ernest Dudeney, edited by Martin Gardner. The game is a variation of the bowling game Kayles, from Dudeney's *The Canterbury Puzzles*.

Coin Chain

MATH CONCEPTS: value of coins, logic, thinking ahead.
PLAYERS: best for two.
EQUIPMENT: ten or more assorted coins.

How to Play

Arrange the coins in a line (straight or curved) so that each coin touches two others, except the coins on the ends of the line will have only one neighbor. Or arrange them in a circle so every coin touches two others.

The youngest player takes the first turn removing a coin. If the coins form a circle, you may choose any coin. On subsequent turns, or if the coins begin in a line, you may choose the coin at either end. Keep the coins you take in a stash pile.

When all the coins are taken, players count the value of their stashes. Whoever has collected the most money wins the game.

History (and a Puzzle)

Alexander Bogomolny posted this coin game online on his Cut the Knot website. In his interactive version, you can choose how many coins you want and play against the computer.

Since both of the players can see all the coins, there is no element of luck in this game. Everything depends o careful planning. What do you think: the first player always win, or does the s player have a chance? Or does it depend on how the coins are arranged?

It's your turn. Should you take the nickel or the penny?

Codebreaker

MATH CONCEPTS: permutations, logical deduction.
PLAYERS: two or more.
EQUIPMENT: paper and pencil, or whiteboard and marker.

How to Play

One player (the *codemaker*) thinks of a three-digit number between 000 and 999, writes this number on a piece of paper, and folds the paper to hide it. The other players (*codebreakers*) draw a two-column chart labeled Guesses and Clues. Players can each keep separate written records, or all may share a single chart on a whiteboard.

The codebreakers take turns guessing a three-digit number, which they record in the guess column. The codemaker responds with the appropriate clues:

♦ If one of the digits is the right number in the right place, say "There's one number correct," and draw a smiley face in the clues column. Do not tell which digit won the smiley.

♦ If one of the digits is a correct number but in the wrong place, say "There's one number right, but it's not where it belongs," and draw an empty circle in the clues column.

My favorite guesses are the ones with nothing right. I know for sure the answer won't have a 1, 2, or 4.

- If more than one digit matches the secret code, tell the total number of correct and almost-right digits—and draw that many smiley faces and plain circles—but never reveal which digit matches which clue.

With two players, a round of play is two numbers, so each player has a chance to be the codemaker. Whoever breaks the code with the fewest guesses wins. For group play, whoever guesses the number gets to be codemaker for the next round.

Variations

For beginners, don't allow repeating digits, and make it easier by using only the numbers 1–5. A secret number like 142 would be fine, but not 223. Advanced players can use four- to six-digit numbers and allow repetition.

Or try playing without paper, keeping track of guesses and clues in your head. This is a mind-bending challenge, but it can be done.

History

In the wee morning hours on a cross-country road trip, I made up the paperless version of Codebreaker to keep the driver awake. In my mind, it was a modification of the commercial board game Mastermind, but according to Wikipedia, similar guessing games with numbers or words date back at least a century.

Chance

MATH CONCEPTS: addition up to three hundred, probability with dice.
PLAYERS: two or more.
EQUIPMENT: five six-sided dice, paper and pencil for keeping score.

How to Play

On your turn, roll all of the dice. Set aside the numbers you would like to keep, and roll the rest of the dice again. If you wish, you may roll once more. After the third roll, add up all the numbers on the dice, and then add that sum to your game score. Pass the dice to the next player. Whoever is the first to reach or pass 300 points wins the game.

Variations

PIG: In the mood for some risk? Using one or two dice, roll as many times as you wish, mentally adding each roll to keep a running total for that turn. You may stop whenever you want and add the total to your score, or keep rolling to collect more points. But if on any roll, either die shows a one, you get zero points for that turn. The two-dice variation has an additional danger: if both dice come up one, all the points you have saved so far disappear, and your game score goes back to zero. The first player to reach or pass 100 points wins the game.

History

Dice games are easy to modify for practicing all sorts of math. Keep a pair of dice in your pocket or bag, and you will always have a way to entertain children (or yourself) in a restaurant or waiting room. Chance is a much-simplified version of the commercial game Yahtzee. Pig is a folk-game cousin to Farkle and was first described in print by American magician and author John Scarne in his 1945 book *Scarne on Dice*.

Forty-Niners

MATH CONCEPTS: addition up to three hundred, probability with playing cards.

PLAYERS: two or more.

EQUIPMENT: one full deck of playing cards (with jokers, if you have them), paper and pencil for keeping score.

How to Play

Shuffle the deck and place it face down where all players can reach. On your turn, pan for gold by flipping over the top card. You can keep going up the stream as long as you dare, turning up new cards in a row and adding together their number values, until you decide to stop. Then add the total to your score, and place your cards in the discard pile.

But if you turn over a face card, your mining camp has been raided by armed bandits, and you score zero for that turn.

If you turn up a joker, the dastardly villain jumps your claim, and you lose all the points you've collected so far. Whenever a joker appears, the dealer reshuffles the whole deck (stock and discards together), so the next player can draw from a freshly randomized pile.

When one player passes the target score of three hundred, all the other players get one last turn. The highest score after this final round wins the game.

History

In 1848, Mexico ceded the California and New Mexico territories to the United States in the treaty that ended the Mexican–American War. That same year, James Marshall discovered gold at Sutter's Mill in Coloma, California. By 1849, news of gold in the mountains east of San Francisco had spread around the world, launching a gold rush that drew people from the Americas, Europe, Australia, and Asia. A few men became rich, but many of the dreamers who traveled west died of shipwreck or disease along the way, and most of those who made it to California ended up poor and discouraged.

For the history of this particular game, see "Mixing It Up" on page 7.

Farkle

MATH CONCEPTS: addition to ten thousand, probability with dice.
PLAYERS: any number.
EQUIPMENT: six six-sided dice, pencil and paper for keeping score.

How to Play

On your turn, throw all six dice. If you like your score (see below for scoring), write it down and pass the dice to the player on your left. Or keep going. But beware: every time you roll the dice, you must set aside at least one scoring die. If none of the dice score, you have farkled, and you lose all the points you have accumulated that turn.

If you get all six dice to score, you have hot dice, and you may roll them all again to continue building up points. If you don't farkle, then whenever you decide to stop rolling, add the points you have collected to your running total for the game. Writing down this score marks the end of your turn.

The first player to reach 10,000 points might win the game. But all the other players get one last chance to try and pass that score without farkling. Highest final score wins.

Scoring the Dice

There is often more than one way to score your dice, and you do not have to set aside every die that could score. Try to keep the highest score you can, while still leaving yourself as many dice as possible to throw again, thus decreasing your risk of a farkle. Every roll is scored separately. If you set aside two ones and then get another one on your next throw, that does not count for 1,000 points.

Each 1 = 100 points
Each 5 = 50
Three 1s = 1,000

Three 2s = 200

Three 3s = 300

Three 4s = 400

Three 5s = 500

Three 6s = 600

Four of a kind = Double the score for three of them

Five of a kind = Double the score for four of them

Six of a kind = Double the score for five of them

Three pairs = 500

Straight (1-2-3-4-5-6) = 1,000

Two triples = 2,500

History

Farkle-style games have been played around the world for centuries, probably since dice were invented. Because of this, rule variants are common, so be sure that all players agree on which version you're playing before the game begins.

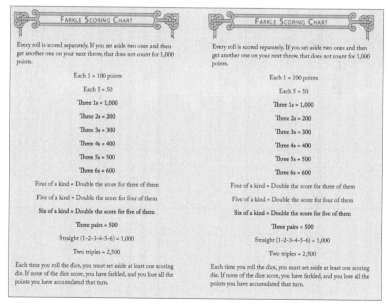

The *Number Game Printables Pack* includes a Farkle scoring guide. Cut the page in half and give one sheet to each player.

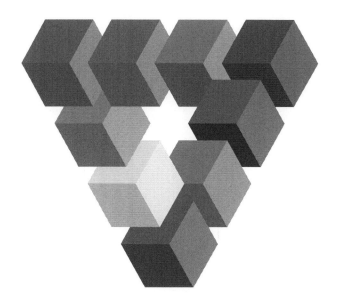

Playing to Learn Math

From the very beginning of his education, the child should experience the joy of discovery.

—ALFRED NORTH WHITEHEAD

Diagnosis: Workbook Syndrome

WHETHER IT IS FICTION, BIOGRAPHY, news, sports, or even just the comics, most of us have something we read for enjoyment. But have you ever done math just for the fun of it, for the joy of discovery?

Many people would consider that a nonsense question. Mathematics has nothing to do with joy. Math is a chore to be endured, like cleaning the bathroom, one of those things that nobody likes but that has to be done.

Isn't it?

Well, no. At least, it doesn't have to be like that.

Our childhood struggles with school math gave most of us a warped view of mathematics. We learned to manipulate numbers and symbols according to what seemed like arbitrary rules. Most of us understood a bit here and a bit there, but we never saw how the framework fit together. We stumbled from one class to the next, packing more and more information into our strained memory, until the whole structure threatened to collapse. Finally we crashed in a blaze of confusion, some of us in high school algebra, others in college calculus.

Now that we are parents and teachers, we see the danger for our children. Many of us dread helping with our children's math homework, not knowing how to explain something that never made sense to us. Homeschoolers switch from one math program to another looking for a magic bullet. Classroom teachers follow the manual faithfully and hope for the best. Or they try a more creative route, scouring professional magazines, websites, and teacher blogs for activities and group projects to supplement the curriculum, hoping something will catch the students' imagination.

Some teaching philosophies recommend a strong focus on memorization in the early grades. Young children, they say, excel at memory work but cannot think logically, so conceptual explanations are wasted on them. Others argue that we must focus on understanding because rote memorization and speed drills can kill a child's interest in mathematics. Some rely on teaching rules and patterns, trusting that insight will follow as these become automatic. Still others push for plenty of hands-on experience that will allow students to draw their own conclusions about how numbers work.

Too often, discussions about math education, at least in America, devolve into a battle of stereotypes and straw-man arguments called the Math Wars.

In our confusion about how to teach mathematics, we have not yet found a way to protect our children from workbook syndrome. What, you may ask, is workbook syndrome? It is a distressing malady that afflicts children in public, private, and home schools across our country. A child suffering from this disease has learned to do calculations on a school math page but cannot make sense of numbers in word problems or in real life.

Mischievous Results of Poor Teaching

Educational pundits may try to blame one side or the other of the Math Wars, but the problem of workbook syndrome goes back at least to the nineteenth century. Victorian educator Charlotte Mason describes the symptoms:

> *There is no one subject in which good teaching effects more, as there is none in which slovenly teaching has more mischievous results.*

Multiplication does not produce the right answer, so the boy tries division; that again fails, but subtraction may get him out of the bog. There is no 'must be' to him — he does not see that one process, and one process only, can give the required result.

Now, a child who does not know what rule to apply to a simple problem within his grasp has been ill taught from the first, although he may produce slatefuls of quite right sums ... The child may learn the multiplication table and do a subtraction sum without any insight into the rationale of either. He may even become a good arithmetician, applying rules aptly, without seeing the reason of them.

I discovered a case of workbook syndrome in math club one afternoon, as I played Multiplication War with a pair of fourth-grade boys. They did fine with the small numbers and knew many of the answers by heart, but they consistently tried to count out the times-nine problems on their fingers. Most of the time, they lost track of what they were counting and ended up wildly wrong.

I stopped the game in midturn to teach a mental math technique: multiplying by nine is the same as multiplying by "ten minus one." Nine of anything is the same as ten of that thing, take away one of them. Nine books is ten books take away a book, and nine horses is ten horses take away one horse. With numbers, 9×6 is ten sixes take away one six, or $60 - 6 = 54$. Similarly, 9×8 is ten eights take away one eight, or $80 - 8 = 72$. It works for any number. For instance, 25×9 is ten twenty-fives take away one twenty-five, or $250 - 25 = 225$. By reducing the multiplication to a much simpler subtraction, this trick makes the times-nine table a cinch.

We spent a few minutes going through the times-nine facts together, just to practice the pattern.

$$1 \times 9 = 10 - 1$$
$$2 \times 9 = 20 - 2$$
$$3 \times 9 = 30 - 3$$
$$4 \times 9 = 40 - 4, \text{etc.}$$

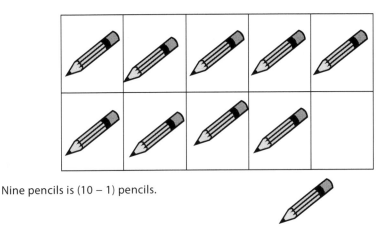

Nine pencils is (10 − 1) pencils.

To my surprise, the older boy could not subtract without counting on his fingers. In several years of classroom training, he had not learned the number bonds, the pairs of numbers that make ten.

No, that can't be true. I am sure he had learned them, probably in kindergarten, but his teachers had never led him to see how these simple facts could help him solve problems, so he had just forgotten them. When I probed further, I found he could not mentally add ten to a two-digit number.

When I gave him a pencil and wrote the numbers on paper, the boy knew how to follow the procedures for adding and subtracting into the thousands and beyond. He'd been taught the standard arithmetic *algorithms*—the traditional set of abstract, multistep rules—yet he had almost no understanding of how numbers work. He had been shafted by several years of poor instruction dished out by teachers who themselves did not understand math.

The Struggle for Balance

We all know that number skills are important to our children's future. As students work their way through elementary and middle school arithmetic, they must:

♦ Understand number concepts, the basic principles of how

numbers work together, such as addition, division, or the distributive property.

♦ Memorize the *math facts*, the simple relationships between small numbers, such as 3 + 5 = 8 and 7 × 2 = 14.

♦ Learn to apply these concepts and facts in an ever-growing variety of situations.

In a well-balanced math education, both components — conceptual understanding and knowledge of basic facts — will grow together. Having number facts in memory makes calculation easier, which allows the students to concentrate on whatever puzzle or problem they are trying to solve. This enables them to add new layers to their understanding and begin to appreciate the more interesting concepts of mathematics. And this new understanding in turn brings new light to the math facts, making them easier to recall.

Unfortunately, I've never found a math program that mixes these components perfectly for my children. My solution has been to pick our math program based on how well it helps my children learn the foundational concepts, knowing I can build in lots of number practice by playing games.

Whatever math curriculum your children use, do not be satisfied with mere pencil-and-paper competence. To prevent workbook syndrome, help your children develop mental math skills. Mental calculation forces a child to understand numbers, because the techniques that let us work with numbers in our heads reinforce the fundamental concepts of arithmetic.

For instance, when my math club boys forgot the times-nine facts, I taught them a technique based on the *distributive property,* one of the most basic principles in math. You can think of it as the shopping bag rule: if you buy fruit in mixed bags, you can take them home and separate the pieces of fruit according to their types. Imagine buying six bags, and each bag contains three apples and two pears. You could say you bought six bags with five pieces of fruit in each bag, 6 × 5 = 30

Don't think of math rules as mere abstractions. They reflect
common sense about how the real world works.

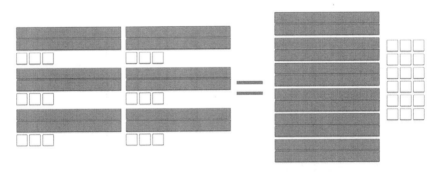

Numbers act just like apples and pears. Six sets of two tens and
three ones (6 × 23) is the same as 6 × 2 tens and 6 × 3 ones.

pieces of fruit. But looking at it by types, you could also say you bought $6 \times 3 = 18$ apples and $6 \times 2 = 12$ pears. When you put that information into a single equation, the parentheses act like grocery bags:

$$\text{Fruit in mixed bags} = \text{fruit sorted by type}$$
$$6 \times (3 + 2) = (6 \times 3) + (6 \times 2)$$

Or if we let a, b, and c represent any numbers:

$$a \times (b + c) = (a \times b) + (a \times c)$$

Be wary of teaching finger tricks, catchy rhymes, or other mnemonic aids that hide what the numbers are doing. Such things burden your child's memory without increasing understanding. For more information about math tricks to avoid, download Tina Cardone's free ebook *Nix the Tricks: A Guide to Avoiding Shortcuts That Cut Out Math Concept Development.*

You can build mental calculation skills by doing math homework orally. To work math problems in their heads, children have to learn how to take numbers apart and put them back together. They figure out ways to simplify calculations and learn to recognize common patterns. The numbers become, in a sense, their friends.

Oral work has another advantage: young children need not be limited by their still-developing fine motor skills. My sons, especially, could advance quickly through math topics that they would never have had the patience to write out. As students progress to more difficult problems, they may wish to have scratch paper or a lap-size whiteboard and colorful markers handy. Even then, however, we do as much work as we can mentally.

As veteran teacher Ruth Beechick writes, "If you stay with meaningful mental arithmetic longer, you will find that your child, if she is average, can do problems much more advanced than the level listed for her grade. You will find that she likes arithmetic more. And when she does get to abstractions, she will understand them better."

Just like the games we play, the fun in learning mathematics is in the challenge.

—Erlina Ronda

Conclusion: Master the Math Facts

When it comes to practicing number facts, many children think math is spelled "b-o-r-i-n-g." Worksheets are tedious, flash cards make them groan, and even the latest computer game is a yawner.

School supply websites feature a variety of educational products designed to make the process easier, from rods and blocks to Math Fact Bingo. Over the years, I have spent hundreds of dollars on products designed to help my children learn math. Maybe a multiplication coloring book with silly stories will help this year, or perhaps we should try a CD of skip-counting songs?

Even children who understand arithmetic well may struggle to master the basic number facts. Learning to understand math is a conceptual task, but learning the math facts is more like rote memory work. Yet rote memory is not enough. A student may recite the times tables perfectly and still be reduced to counting on fingers in the middle of a long-division problem.

Training one's mind to recall answers when needed is a lot like learning to type. It comes in stages.

Stage One: Hunt and Peck

In typing, we understand that we have to push down the proper key to get the letter we want, but it may take us a few minutes to find that key. In math, this is the manipulative or counting-on-fingers stage.

Stage Two: Slow but Steady

Now we have learned that each finger controls certain keys, but we have to think about whether "c" is up or down from the home row. In math, students understand the concepts behind each math fact, but they still count by five to calculate 5×7.

Stage Three: Automatic Response

Professional typists look at a word on the paper they are copying, and their fingers automatically hit the proper sequence of keys. Typing has become a reflex. A math student who has reached this stage can see 2×5 on a worksheet and instantly think "10."

Of course, we do not progress evenly from one stage to the next. As a typist, I work primarily in stage two, but simple words (*the* or *and*) are automatic, while I still hunt and peck the numbers and unusual forms of punctuation. For our students, progress in learning math will come the same, slow way. They may know instantly that 3×5 is the same as 15, while they still count on their fingers to solve monsters like 8×6.

Also, notice that not all typists reach the automatic stage. I have a friend who can type more than one hundred words per minute, almost as fast as she can think. I can type around thirty words per minute, which is about as fast as I can think, too. Would I like to type faster? Sure, but not enough to work at it. I will never be a medical transcriptionist, but I can type well enough for email.

In the same way, not every student will reach the automatic stage with all the number facts. Most of us still struggle with remembering a few of them as adults, often the times-seven or times-eight facts. As long as we know how to figure out the ones we cannot recall, we will survive.

As with typing, there is only one way to reach the automatic stage: practice, practice, practice. The student must calculate the number relationships over and over and over, so many times that the correct response becomes a reflex. Practice makes permanent.

Thankfully, with the games in the *Math You Can Play* series, practicing the math facts can be fun.

A Strategy for Learning

There is no perfect teacher. There is only you and me, and we have no superpowers. We can't save the world or solve the latest crisis of educational policy.

But we can help our children learn to do mental math. We can encourage them to practice strategic thinking and develop problem-solving skills. We can prevent (or treat) math anxiety and build a positive attitude toward learning.

So what are we waiting for? Let's play some math!

Resources and References

Game-Playing Basics, From Set-Up to Endgame

WHEN I WAS A CHILD, I assumed that whatever I knew was common knowledge and anything I believed was common sense. Now I have grown up enough to realize how very much I do not know. So I understand how confusing new ideas (or new games) can be.

Below I summarize everything I can think of that might be assumed-but-never-explained about playing games in the *Math You Can Play* series. If you have a question I didn't answer, please send me an email.[†]

Math Concepts

Most of the *Math You Can Play* games build your students' skill at working with numbers in their heads. Some games focus on one or two concepts, while others cover a wide range of ideas. The latter are not necessarily better than the former.

Players

Almost all of the games are designed for two or more competing players, but a few can also work as solitaire games. If a game relies primarily on chance, it usually does not matter how many people are playing, but the more strategy involved in a game, the more likely it will work best as a two-player battle of minds.

When playing with a larger group, it may work better to split up and play separate games so players don't have too much idle time between their turns. Waiting patiently can be difficult for an adult, so we shouldn't be surprised that it's hard for children.

If you are playing with a wide range of skill levels, avoid games that rely on

---

† *LetsPlayMath@gmail.com*

speed or modify them to allow each player adequate time to think. In some cases, you may allow extra turns to the younger students. For instance, in Concentration (Memory), you might let younger children turn up three cards instead of the usual two, giving them a better chance to find a pair that match.

Who goes first? Sometimes there is an advantage to going first in a game, so I often let the youngest player go first. You can randomize the turns by letting each player throw a die or draw one card from the deck, and then whoever gets the highest number goes first. In multiplayer card games, whoever gets the lowest number is the dealer, and the player sitting to the dealer's left goes first.

Shuffle and Cut

In card or domino games, the players must thoroughly mix the cards or tiles to ensure randomness. Any player may shuffle, but in card games, the dealer has the right to shuffle last. Players should not try to sneak a peek during the shuffle, and to take advantage of an accidentally revealed card is cheating.

The riffle shuffle (in which a deck of cards is split in half and then the halves are interlaced) takes plenty of practice, but it is the best way to quickly randomize the cards. It takes about seven riffles to fully shuffle a deck. If you've never seen a riffle shuffle, search YouTube for a video that demonstrates the technique.[†]

For young children, the easiest way to shuffle is domino style. Spread all the cards face down on the table, mix them around, and then stack them up again without looking.

If only the dealer shuffles the cards, it is polite to offer another player (usually whoever is to the dealer's right, opposite the direction of the deal) the chance to cut the deck. The player splits the deck into two parts, with at least four cards in each part, places the top part on the table without looking at it, and then stacks the other part on top of it. Thus neither player nor dealer can know the exact position of any card.

Deal and Rotation of Play

In many card games, one person—the dealer—will hand out cards to each player in turn, going around the table in the direction of play. The dealer may give one card at a time, or two or more at once, but should deal the same to

---

† *For example, youtu.be/3oabnbtJRNQ.*

The riffle shuffle is an efficient way to randomize a deck of cards.

every player. Out of politeness and to avoid putting other players at a disadvantage, everyone should wait until all cards are dealt before picking up and looking at their hands.

My family plays by the tradition common in the United States that the deal and the players' turns go to the left (clockwise) around the table. I have read that many countries do the opposite, rotating play to the right. For the games in this book, direction does not matter, so use whichever seems comfortable to you.

Hand vs. Round vs. Game

The cards a player holds are called his or her hand. These are normally kept hidden from the other players until used in the game. Children often need to be reminded to hold their hands close to their bodies so that the other players do not see their cards.

One complete section of a game, where every player has a turn or chance to play, may be called a hand or a round. Sometimes the terms are interchangeable, but for more complicated games it may take several hands to make a round and several rounds to finish a complete game.

Draw Pile (Stock) and Discard Pile

In games where players will need to refresh their hands, the remainder of the deck (after cards have been dealt) is turned face down and placed on the table where everyone can reach. This is the *stock* or *draw pile*.

The unwanted cards from the players' hands are often turned face up next to the draw pile, either as a single stack or fanned out so all are visible. In some games, these discards may be available for other players to use in subsequent turns.

In many games for young children, a *fishing pond* is used in place of a draw pile. Turn all the cards face down and spread them out to form a roughly circular area where all players can reach. On their turns, players may choose any card. Discards should be thoroughly mixed back into the pond before the next player's turn, so that nobody can remember their location.

Misdeal and Other Irregularities

When playing with children, you can almost guarantee that misdeals or exposed cards will happen. Some traditional games specify harsh penalties for such irregularities—think of old Western movies, where a game of poker could break into a bar fight or shootout over a simple mistake. In a family game, we can be more lenient. Our children must learn that cheating ruins the game for everyone, but there is no shame in an unintended error.

If the dealer inadvertently gives the wrong number of cards to a player or accidentally exposes a card that other players are not supposed to see, just fix the misdeal in a way that seems fair all around, either by mixing the offending cards back into the deck or by reshuffling and starting over. If the players have looked at their hands before realizing they have too many cards, no one should choose which of his or her own cards to give back. If dealing again seems like too much trouble, players can fan out their hands and let the dealer or another player who can't see the cards pick and discard the extras.

In the same way, anything wrong that happens in a game should be resolved in such a way as seems fair to every player. For example, if someone plays a card out of turn or starts to make an illegal play, the exposed card should stay face up on the table and be used at the next legal opportunity. Or if the deck is bad (perhaps the players discover that a few cards are missing), the current hand should start over with a new deck, but any points that have been recorded from previous rounds should stand.

Keeping Score

At our house, we often play for the next deal, rather than for points. My children enjoy having control over the game, so getting to deal is a treat for them. When we do play for points, the kids love to use poker chips to keep score: white = 1 point, red = 5 points, and blue = 10 points.

You could let your children practice money skills by using coins to keep score. Give one penny per point, with players trading in for higher coins as they progress, and the first player to collect $1 (or $5 or $10) wins the game.

Or you may use face cards and jokers as tallies in games where the winner of each hand gets a point. Give one tally card per point until they are gone, and whoever collects the most cards is the champion. Since there are three face cards in each of the four suits, this will make a total of twelve hands, or fourteen with both jokers.

Or Try a Cribbage Board

You can often pick up cards, dice, dominoes, and poker chips at garage sales for next to nothing. A rarer discovery worth grabbing if you see one is a cribbage board (sometimes called a *crib board*). You don't have to know how to play cribbage to find this useful. It can be a great way to record points in many different games.

Keep score using two small pegs in leapfrog fashion. Each hole represents a point, and the holes are arranged in groups of five for easy counting. To record your first score, count that many holes and place your first peg. For the second score, leave the first peg where it is and count beyond it, placing

A 60-point cribbage board for two players.
Move the pegs away from yourself up your first row of thirty holes
and then back down the second row. Use the holes in the middle
for longer games, to count your trips around the board.

the second peg at your new total. For each succeeding set of points, leave the farthest-advanced peg in place to guard against losing count, and jump the other peg past it to the new total. The first player to peg out—that is, to reach the last hole—wins the game.

If you buy it used, your cribbage board may have lost its pegs. You can snip the sharp ends off round toothpicks or use wooden matchsticks as makeshift cribbage pegs.

A three-player cribbage board for a game of 120 points.
Follow your own line of holes around the loop to the
end.If you use the three extra holes to count trips
around the board, you can play longer games.

A Few of My Favorite Resources

IF YOU KNOW OF A fantastic math games resource I missed, please send me an email. I appreciate your help!

Best-Loved Books

Most of these books should be available through your local library or via inter-library loan. Check for recreational games in the 793–795 range in the Dewey decimal system, and look for elementary education games at 372.

Camp Logic by Mark Saul and Sian Zelbo

Family Math by Jean Kerr Stenmark, Virginia Thompson, and Ruth Cossey

Games for Math by Peggy Kaye

Games with Pencil and Paper by Eric Solomon

Hexaflexagons and Other Mathematical Diversions and other books by Martin Gardner

Math for Smarty Pants and *The 'I Hate Mathematics!' Book* by Marilyn Burns

Math Games and Activities from Around the World and other books by Claudia Zaslavsky

Mathematical Activities: A Resource Book for Teachers and *The Amazing Mathematical Amusement Arcade* and other books by Brian Bolt

Moebius Noodles: Adventurous Math for the Playground Crowd by Yelena McManaman and Maria Droujkova

Playing with Math: Stories from Math Circles, Homeschoolers, and Passionate Teachers edited by Sue VanHattum

Online Games and Resources

The Internet overflows with a wide-ranging assortment of math websites. The list on my website is much longer than this, and the "good intentions" folder of links I hope to add someday is longer still.

AMBLEWEB FUNCTION MACHINE: Choose the type of problem you want to guess, or go random for more challenge. My math club kids love function machines.
ambleside primary.com/ambleweb/mentalmaths/functionmachines.html

CUT THE KNOT INTERACTIVE: "Mathematics Miscellany and Puzzles," one of my all-time favorite sites. See also "Math Games and Puzzles, A Short Illustrated List."
cut-the-knot.org
cut-the-knot.org/games.shtml

DAILY TREASURE: Solve the logic puzzle to find the hidden gold.
4chests.blogspot.com

GAMES AND MATH AND PAM SOROOSHIAN ON DICE: Math itself is a game we play.
sandradodd.com/math/pamgames
sandradodd.com/math/pamdice

HEAD HUNTERS GAME: A bloody fun game for the Viking in all of us. If you enjoy that one, try the other math tricks and games at Murderous Maths.
murderousmaths.co.uk/games/headhunt/headhunt.htm
murderousmaths.co.uk

INCOMPETECH: Free online graph paper PDFs galore for any math game.
incompetech.com/graphpaper

Many interactive math websites require Java or Adobe Flash. Unfortunately, both programs can also be used by hackers to break into your computer or do other nasty stuff. Make sure you have the most recent versions of each program, and keep your security settings up to date.

java.com
java.com/en/download/help/java_blocked.xml
java.com/en/download/faq/exception_sitelist.xml
adobe.com/products/flashplayer.html

KenKen for Teachers: A playful way to practice arithmetic.
kenkenpuzzle.com/teachers/classroom

Math Pickle: Videos introduce fun and challenging printable games/puzzles for K–12 students. Can your students solve the $1,000,000 problems?
mathpickle.com

Math Playground: My favorite site for a variety of math games.
mathplayground.com

Math Worksheet Site: My personal favorite hundred chart generator.
themathworksheetsite.com

Mathematical Games and Recreations: "The whole history of mathematics is interwoven with mathematical games which have led to the study of many areas of mathematics."
www-groups.dcs.st-and.ac.uk/~history/HistTopics/Mathematical_games.html

Moebius Noodles: Plenty of ideas for sharing rich math experiences with your children.
moebiusnoodles.com

Nrich.maths.org: A wonderful source of math games and activities for all ages, with a theme that changes each month.
nrich.maths.org/public/index.php

Pagat.com: Pagat is a wonderful collection of card game rules and variations from around the world. Great fun to browse.
pagat.com

Recreational Mathematics: Games, art, humor, and more.
mathworld.wolfram.com/topics/RecreationalMathematics.html

Rush Hour Online: A fun logic puzzle game.
puzzles.com/products/RushHour/RHfromMarkRiedel/Jam.html

Scratch: A programming language that makes it easy for students to create interactive stories, animations, games, music, and art.
scratch.mit.edu

All the website links in this book were checked in April 2015, but the Internet is volatile. If the website disappears, you can run a browser search for the author's name or article title. Or try entering the web address at the Internet Archive Wayback Machine.
archive.org/web/web.php

SET DAILY PUZZLE: Logic puzzle game for all ages.
setgame.com/set/puzzle_frame.htm

TAXICAB TREASURE HUNT: A game based on the non-Euclidean geometry of city streets.
learner.org/teacherslab/math/geometry/shape/taxicab/index.html

ULTIMATE LIST OF PRINTABLE MATH MANIPULATIVES & GAMES: A treasure list from one of my favorite homeschooling blogs.
jimmiescollage.com/2011/04/ultimate-list-of-printable-math-manipulatives-games

Board Games for Family Play

Board games are a celebration of problem solving, and problem solving is at the heart of a quality mathematics education. The mathematics might be hidden, but I guarantee you that it will be there.
—GORDON HAMILTON

In addition to the classics of strategy—backgammon, chess, mancala, Othello/Reversi, Pente, and so on—your family can enjoy (and learn from) many modern games:

BLOKUS: Strategy game for up to four players.

CARCASSONNE: Lay down your tiles to create a landscape based on southern France.

CITADELS: Bluffing, deduction, and city-building set in a medieval world.

DVONN: An abstract strategy game based on moving pieces to make the largest stack.

FOR SALE: Buy and sell real estate to amass your fortune.

FORBIDDEN ISLAND: Capture four sacred treasures from the ruins of this perilous paradise.

KING OF TOKYO: Mutant monsters, gigantic robots, and other aliens vie for the right to rule the city.

LABYRINTH: Find a path to collect your treasures, but watch out—the maze shifts and changes on every turn.

Lost Cities: Explore the world in search of ancient civilizations.

Love Letter: A short, simple game that combines luck and strategy.

Memoir '44: Test your strategic skills as you refight the battles of World War II.

Mr. Jack: Jack the Ripper is loose in Whitechapel, and it's up to you to stop him.

Munchkin Quest: Explore the dungeon and battle monsters for power and treasure.

Power Grid: Acquire raw materials, upgrade your power plants, and expand your network to more cities.

Quarto: Four-in-a-row strategy game.

Quirkle: Strategically match colors and shapes to build up your score.

Quoridor: Move your pawn through the maze, and block the other players.

Set: Visual perception card game.

Settlers of Catan: A trading and building game set in a mythical world.

7 Wonders: Lead an ancient civilization as it rises from its barbaric roots to become a world power.

Smash Up: Easy to learn, fun to play, and always different.

Splendor: As a Renaissance merchant, you must acquire mines and transportation, hire artisans, and woo the nobility.

Stone Age: Gather resources to feed and shelter your tribe.

Ticket to Ride: A cross-country train adventure. How many cities can you visit?

Zeus on the Loose: Use addition, subtraction, and strategic thinking to capture the runaway god.

Zooloretto: Plan carefully to attract as many visitors as possible to your zoo.

APPENDIX C

Quotes and Reference Links

I LOVE QUOTATIONS. EVERYTHING I could ever want to say has probably been said sometime by someone else (who did not think of it first, either). At least a few of those people had a wonderful way with words.

Some of the quotations in this book are from my own reading. Others are gleaned from two websites that I visit often to browse: Furman University's Mathematical Quotation Server and the Mathematical and Educational Quotation Server at Westfield State College.†

ANONYMOUS. "We do not stop playing because we grow old…" Attributed to Benjamin Franklin, Oliver Wendell Holmes, and George Bernard Shaw, among others. Choose your favorite sage.

APOLLO. "Bowling Score Sheets," Apollo's Templates website. *apollostemplates.com/templates-bowling*

BEECHICK, RUTH. "If you stay with meaningful mental arithmetic…" from *An Easy Start in Arithmetic (Grades K–3),* Arrow Press, 1986.

BERLEKAMP, ELWYN R, JOHN H CONWAY, AND RICHARD K GUY. *Winning Ways for Your Mathematical Plays,* A. K. Peters Ltd., 4 vols., 2001–2004.

BLOCK, NADINE. "Dollar Nim," shared by Patrick Vennebush at Math Jokes 4 Mathy Folks blog, June 27, 2011. *mathjokes4mathyfolks.wordpress.com/2011/06/27/dollar-nim*

BOGOMOLNY, ALEXANDER. "A Game with Coins," Cut the Knot website. *cut-the-knot.org/Curriculum/Games/Coins.shtml*

—. "Math Games and Puzzles: A Short Illustrated List," Cut the Knot website. *cut-the-knot.org/games.shtml*

---

† *math.furman.edu/~mwoodard/mquot.html*
westfield.ma.edu/math/faculty/fleron/quotes

BROADBENT, F W. "Contig: A Game to Practice and Sharpen Skills and Facts in the Four Fundamental Operations," *The Arithmetic Teacher*, May 1972.
jstor.org/stable/41188047
maconpiattroe.org/vimages/shared/vnews/stories/54c95745dbc67/Contig%20Rules.pdf

BRODSKY, JULIA. "One of my objectives..." from "The Art of Inquiry: A Very Young Math Circle," in *Playing with Math: Stories from Math Circles, Homeschoolers, and Passionate Teachers*, edited by Sue VanHattum, Delta Stream Media, 2015. Brodsky is a homeschooling mom, former astronaut instructor for NASA, and the creative force behind The Art of Inquiry math circle in Maryland.
playingwithmath.org

BURNS, MARILYN. *About Teaching Mathematics*, 3rd ed., Math Solutions Publications, 2007.

CARDONE, TINA. *Nix the Tricks: A Guide to Avoiding Shortcuts that Cut Out Math Concept Development*, self-published, 2013.
nixthetricks.com

CARLTON, JEAN. "Domino Cover-Up," shared by Alice P. Wakefield in *Early Childhood Number Games: Teachers Reinvent Math Instruction*, Allyn & Bacon, 1998.

COLE, A J, AND A J T DAVIE. "A Game Based on the Euclidean Algorithm and a Winning Strategy for It," *The Mathematical Gazette*, vol. 53 (1969), no. 386, 354–357.

DANIELSON, CHRISTOPHER. *Talking Math with Your Kids*, self-published, 2013, and Talking Math with Your Kids blog.
talkingmathwithkids.com

DONNE, JOHN. "No man is an island..." from "Meditation 17," *Devotions upon Emergent Occasions*, 1623; excerpt available at Wikisource, full text at Project Gutenberg.
en.wikisource.org/wiki/Meditation_XVII
gutenberg.org/ebooks/23772

DUDENEY, H E. *The Canterbury Puzzles*, Thomas Nelson and Sons, 1919 (originally published 1907); available at Project Gutenberg.
gutenberg.org/ebooks/27635

—, EDITED BY MARTIN GARDNER. *536 Puzzles and Curious Problems,* Charles Scribner's Sons, 1967.

ERNEST, JAMES. "Gold Digger," Cheapass Games website. Printable rules and playing cards.
cheapass.com/free-games/gold-digger

—. "Pennywise," Cheapass Games website. Printable sheet available with additional rules and variations.
cheapass.com/free-games/pennywise

GARDNER, MARTIN. "Jam, Hot, and Other Games," in *Mathematical Carnival,* Alfred A. Knopf, 1975. See also Mahoney, John F.

GARELICK, BARRY. "The amazement I felt at…" from "Confessions of a Math Major," *Math Education in the U.S.: Still Crazy After All These Years,* self-published, 2016. Originally published at Education News website, April 13, 2010. Quoted by Joanne Jacobs at her Linking and Thinking on Education blog.
*web.archive.org/web/20100418202219/educationnews.org/
    commentaries/89429.html*
joannejacobs.com/2010/04/confessions-of-a-math-major

GASKINS, DENISE. *Let's Play Math: How Families Can Learn Math Together, and Enjoy It,* Tabletop Academy Press, 2016.

—. "Number Game Printables Pack," Tabletop Academy Press website.
tabletopacademy.net/free-printables

—. "Pondering Large Numbers," Let's Play Math blog, Nov. 26, 2013.
denisegaskins.com/2013/11/26/pondering-large-numbers

—. "Things to Do with a Hundred Chart," Let's Play Math blog, Sept. 22, 2008.
denisegaskins.com/2008/09/22/things-to-do-hundred-chart

GOLDEN, JOHN. "Be careful! There are a lot of useless games…" from "Math Games for Skills and Concepts," PDF handout, Math Hombre blog. Golden helps train future math teachers as an associate professor at Grand Valley State University, and trains the rest of us through the posts on his blog.
faculty.gvsu.edu/goldenj/GameshandoutHS.pdf

—. "Games Reference Page," Math Hombre blog.
mathhombre.blogspot.com/p/games.html

—with Nicholas Smith. "Make and Take," Math Hombre blog, Nov. 11, 2011.
mathhombre.blogspot.com/2011/11/make-and-take.html

—. "Money Games," Math Hombre blog, Aug. 4, 2009.
mathhombre.blogspot.com/2009/08/money-games.html

Graff, Holly. "The most profound learning often takes place silently and invisibly..." from "One and a Quarter Pizzas: An Unschooling Adventure," in *Playing with Math: Stories from Math Circles, Homeschoolers, and Passionate Teachers,* edited by Sue VanHattum, Delta Stream Media, 2015. Graff is a former public school science teacher who blogs at Unschool Days.
playingwithmath.org
unschoolgirls.blogspot.com

Greene, Joshua. "Dice mining (grades 2 and 3 math)," Three J's Learning blog, July 8, 2015.
3jlearneng.blogspot.com/2015/07/dice-mining-grades-2-and-3-math.html

Halabi, Jonathan. "A child learns to count spoonfuls..." from "Pedagogy: Outlook on teaching math," Jd2718 blog, Jan. 21, 2007. Halabi is a high school math teacher who blogs about education, math, teaching, New York, the Bronx, teachers unions, language, and travel.
jd2718.org/2007/01/21/pedagogy-outlook-on-teaching-math

Hamilton, Gordon. "Board games are a celebration..." from "Commercial Games," YouTube video, Dec. 25, 2011. Hamilton posts games and activity ideas for all ages at his Math Pickle website.
youtu.be/J8geFOkOUbU
mathpickle.com

Hockman-Chupp, Cynthia. "Subitizing—Making Sense of Numbers," Love 2 Learn 2 Day blog, April 21, 2012.
love2learn2day.blogspot.com/2012/04/subitizing-making-sense-of-numbers.html

Kamii, Constance, with Leslie Baker Housman. *Young Children Reinvent Arithmetic: Implications of Piaget's Theory,* 2nd ed., Teachers College Press, 2000.

—with Linda Leslie Joseph. *Young Children Continue to Reinvent Arithmetic, 2nd Grade: Implications of Piaget's Theory,* 2nd ed., Teachers College Press, 2004.

—with Sally Jones Livingston. *Young Children Continue to Reinvent Arithmetic, 3rd Grade: Implications of Piaget's Theory,* Teachers College Press, 1994.

KAWAS, TERRY. "Contig Jr.," MathWire website, 2009.
mathwire.com/games/contigjr.pdf

KAYE, PEGGY. "Children learn more math and enjoy math more…" from *Games for Math,* Pantheon Books, 1988. If you're homeschooling young children, be sure to check out the other books in Kaye's *Games for…* series.
peggykaye.com

LA TOUCHE, MARIA PRICE. "I do hate sums…" from *The Letters of A Noble Woman,* George Allen & Sons, London, 1908; available at Internet Archive.
archive.org/details/lettersofnoblewo00latorich

LEO, LUCINDA. "With any curriculum there is the temptation…" from "Things I've Learned About Homeschooling," Navigating by Joy blog, Dec. 10, 2013. Leo is an English mom who blogs about her family's unschooling adventures.
*navigatingbyjoy.com/2013/12/10/3-things-ive-learned-
homeschooling-2013*

MAHONEY, JOHN F. "What is the Name of This Game?" *Mathematics Teaching in the Middle School,* vol. 11 (2005), no. 3, 150–154.
nctm.org/uploadedFiles/Lessons_and_Resources/p150-154.pdf

MASON, CHARLOTTE. "There is no one subject…" from *Home Education,* 5th ed., 1906 (originally published 1886); available at Internet Archive. Mason encouraged parents to focus on word problems that build reasoning skills, to emphasize mental work over written sums, and to allow free access to manipulatives as long as the child found them helpful.
archive.org/details/homeeducationser01masouoft

McGLOHN, SHARON. "Phone Number Cover-Up," shared by Alice P. Wakefield in *Early Childhood Number Games: Teachers Reinvent Math Instruction,* Allyn & Bacon, 1998.

McLEOD, JOHN. "Card Game Rules: Card Games and Tile Games from around the World," Pagat website. Pagat is a wonderful collection of card game rules and variations from around the world. Great fun to browse.
pagat.com

—. "Card Bingo," Pagat website, Oct. 31, 2011.
pagat.com/banking/bingo.html

—. "Euchre," Pagat website, Aug. 16, 2013.
pagat.com/euchre/euchre.html

MEYER, DAN. "Tiny Math Games," dy/dan blog, April 16, 2013.
blog.mrmeyer.com/2013/tiny-math-games

MEYER, MARK. "Nim-values in Fibonacci Nim," academic paper, University of Minnesota, Morris, Spring 2010.
facultypages.morris.umn.edu/math/Ma4901/Sp2010/Final/MarkMeyer-final.pdf

MIGHTON, JOHN. "A hundred years ago..." from *The Myth of Ability: Nurturing Mathematical Talent in Every Child,* Walker & Company, 2003.

NRICH TEAM. "Stop or Dare," Nrich Enriching Mathematics website.
nrich.maths.org/1193

PARDUN, JIM. The Calendar Game is from comment #39 on Dan Meyer's "Tiny Math Games," dy/dan blog, April 16, 2013. Pardun is a high school math teacher and author of the blog Teaching From The Heart, Not The Book.
blog.mrmeyer.com/2013/tiny-math-games
jimpardun.wordpress.com

PATTERSON, GEOFF. "Fibonacci Nim," School and University Partnership for Educational Renewal in Mathematics, University of Hawai'i Department of Mathematics.
superm.math.hawaii.edu/_pdfs/lessons/k_five/SuperM_Nim.pdf

PLATO. "There should be no element of slavery in learning..." from *The Republic.* Quoted at the Mathematical and Educational Quotation Server at Westfield State University.
westfield.ma.edu/math/faculty/fleron/quotes/viewquote.asp?letter=p

RAMANI, GEETHA B, AND ROBERT S SIEGLER. "Promoting Broad and Stable Improvements in Low-Income Children's Numerical Knowledge Through Playing Number Board Games," *Child Development,* vol. 79 (2008), no. 2, 375–394.
psy.cmu.edu/~siegler/Ram-Sieg2008.pdf

REULBACH, JULIE. "Math Games Collection on Google Docs—Add Your Game Today!" I Speak Math blog, November 18, 2013.
ispeakmath.org/2013/11/18/math-games-collection-on-google-docs-add-your-game-to-day

RONDA, ERLINA R. "Just like the games we play..." from "The fun in learning mathematics is in the challenge," Mathematics for Teaching blog, Nov. 2, 2011. Ronda is a mathematics education specialist at the University of the

Philippines and also writes a math puzzle blog for students, K–12 Math Problems.

math4teaching.com/fun-in-learning-mathematics-challenge
math-problems.math4teaching.com

ROWINSKY, NICO. "Chopsticks," comment #23 on Dan Meyer's "Tiny Math Games," dy/dan blog, April 16, 2013. Rowinsky teaches middle school math in Canada and blogs at Y_0: A Math Teacher's Blog.

blog.mrmeyer.com/2013/tiny-math-games
ynaughtmath.blogspot.ca

SCARNE, JOHN, WITH CLAYTON RAWSON. *Scarne on Dice,* Military Service Publishing Co., 1945.

SIEGLER, ROBERT S, AND GEETHA B RAMANI. "Playing Linear Number Board Games—But Not Circular Ones—Improves Low-Income Pre-schoolers' Numerical Understanding," *Journal of Educational Psychology,* vol. 101 (2009), no. 3, 545–560.

psy.cmu.edu/~siegler/sieg-ram09.pdf

SOROOSHIAN, PAM. "Mathematicians don't sit around..." from the old Unschooling Discussion Yahoo group, quoted by Sandra Dodd in "Games and Math," Sandra Dodd's Unschoolers and Mathematics website.

sandradodd.com/math/pamgames

—. "Pam Sorooshian on Dice," Sandra Dodd's Unschoolers and Mathematics website.

sandradodd.com/math/pamdice

SOUSA, DAVID A. "Mathematical competence involves..." from *How the Brain Learns Mathematics,* Corwin Press, 2008.

TANTON, JAMES. "Math is the beautiful, rich, joyful..." from "Philosophy of this Site," Thinking Mathematics website, 2009. Tanton is a mathematician and educator who brings the creative joy of math to his students. Check out his free online video courses at G'Day Math.

jamestanton.com/wp-content/uploads/2009/04/philosophy-of-site-essay.pdf
gdaymath.com

—. "Partition Numbers: An Accessible Overview," Thinking Mathematics website, Feb. 25, 2011.

jamestanton.com/?p=892

VanHattum, Sue. "People have this notion…" from "Richmond Math Salon: A Sweet Sampling," Math Mama Writes… blog, Aug. 8, 2010. VanHattum is a community college mathematics teacher, math circle leader, and blogger.
mathmamawrites.blogspot.com/2010/08/richmond-math-salon-sweet-sampling_08.html

—. *Playing with Math: Stories from Math Circles, Homeschoolers, and Passionate Teachers,* Delta Stream Media, 2015.
playingwithmath.org

Vennebush, Patrick. "Dollar Nim," Math Jokes 4 Mathy Folks blog, June 27, 2011.
mathjokes4mathyfolks.wordpress.com/2011/06/27/dollar-nim

Wakefield, Alice P. *Early Childhood Number Games: Teachers Reinvent Math Instruction,* Allyn & Bacon, 1998.

Way, Jenni. "Games can allow children to operate…" from "Learning Mathematics Through Games Series: 1. Why Games?," Nrich Enriching Mathematics website. Way is a math education researcher and associate professor at the University of Sydney.
nrich.maths.org/2489

Wedd, Nick, and John McLeod. "Mechanics of Card Games," Pagat website, May 15, 2009.
pagat.com/mech.html

Weltman, Anna. "Snugglenumber," Recipes for π blog, Oct. 16, 2013. Weltman teaches elementary, middle, and high school math at Saint Ann's School in Brooklyn, N.Y.
recipesforpi.wordpress.com/2013/10/16/snugglenumber

Whinihan, M J. "Fibonacci Nim," *Fibonacci Quarterly,* vol. 1 (1963), no. 4, 9–13. Referenced in Meyer, "Nim-values in Fibonacci Nim," see above.

Whitehead, Alfred North. "From the very beginning of his education…" from "The Aims of Education," in *The Aims of Education and Other Essays,* Macmillan Company, 1929. Whitehead was an English mathematician and philosopher and coauthor (with Bertrand Russell) of *Principia Mathematica.*
anthonyflood.com/whiteheadeducation.htm

Wikipedia Contributors. "Bulls and cows," Wikipedia Internet Encyclopedia.

en.wikipedia.org/wiki/Bulls_and_cows

——. "Gold rush," Wikipedia Internet Encyclopedia.
en.wikipedia.org/wiki/Gold_rush

——. "Pig (dice game)," Wikipedia Internet Encyclopedia.
en.wikipedia.org/wiki/Pig_%28dice_game%29

——. "Shut the Box," Wikipedia Internet Encyclopedia.
en.wikipedia.org/wiki/Shut_the_Box

ZASLAVSKY, CLAUDIA. "Language should be part of the activity..." from *Preparing Young Children for Mathematics: A Book of Games with Updated Book, Game and Resource Lists,* Schocken Books, 1986. Any book by Zaslavsky is well worth reading.

Index

math concepts (*continued*)
    ill-defined problems, 129
    logic, 129
    number bonds, 52, 83
    number line, 67
    subitizing, 18
    subtraction related to addition, 83
    whole is made up of parts, 83
math concepts in games
    addition beyond one hundred,
        137–138, 140
    addition to one hundred, 103, 105,
        137
    addition to twenty, 87, 90, 92, 95, 97,
        132
    calendar, 68
    calendar dates, 108
    coins, value of, 106, 134, 163
    column addition, 125
    counting beyond ten, 27, 68, 70
    counting down, 43
    counting up to ten, 21, 23
    dot patterns, 25, 47
    how to read a hundred chart, 70
    less than or greater than, 35, 71, 90
    logical deduction, 130, 135
    matching attributes, 37
    matching sets, 25
    multistep calculation, 118, 120, 122,
        125
    number bonds, 55, 57, 61, 85, 87
    number bonds for ten, 59, 60
    number line, 27, 132
    number patterns, 109
    number symbols, 27, 29, 33
    numerical order, 29, 41, 73
    permutations, 135
    place value, 73, 75, 111
    probability, 75
    probability (cards), 111, 138
    probability (dice), 132, 137, 140
    rank of playing cards, 41, 43
    sorting by attribute, 41, 43
    strategic guessing, 71
    subitizing, 23, 25, 47

math concepts in games (*continued*)
    subtraction to one hundred, 106, 108
    subtraction to twenty, 90, 95
    variables, 37
    visual/spatial memory, 25, 85
math facts, 150
    mastery of, 154
math for the fun of it, 146
"Math Games for Classrooms", 105, 175
math is beautiful, xiii
Math Jokes 4 Mathy Folks, 107
Math War Trumps, 91
Math Wars, 147
Mathematical Carnival, 93, 172
mathematical competence, 99
mathematicians play games, 8
McGlohn, Sharon, 63, 89, 174
McLeod, John, 34, 174
memorization
    like learning to type, 154
    mnemonic aids, 152
    rote memory, 81
    young children and, 53, 84, 147
mental math
    add in chunks, 116
    benefits of, 4, 152
    builds on number bonds, 100
    friendly numbers, 100, 116
    funny numbers, 100
    highest place value first, 100
    move the pieces, 100
    offering a hint, 117
    oral homework, 152
    pose a simpler problem, 116
    times-nine trick, 148
mental number line, 66
messed-up labels, 130
Meyer, Dan, 22, 69, 108, 175
Michigan (Boodle), 41
Mighton, John, 51, 175
Millennium Mathematics Project, 95
mischievous results of poor teaching, 147
misdeals, 162
misère game, 69, 107
modifying games, 7

Reulbach, Julie, 105, 175
Ronda, Erlina, 154, 175
rote memory, 81, 147, 154
Rowinsky, Nico, 22, 176
rules
    dealing the cards, 160
    discard pile, 162
    don't peek!, 161
    draw pile (stock), 162
    fishing pond, 162
    hand vs. round vs. game, 161
    house rules, 14
    keeping score, 163
    learn by playing, 14
    misdeal and other mistakes, 162
    number of players, 159
    rotation of play, 160
    shuffle and cut, 160
    variations, 7
    who goes first?, 160

S

Scarne on Dice, 137, 176
Scarne, John, 137, 176
sciolist, 115
shopping bag rule, 150
shuffling cards, 160
Shut the Box, 61, 87
Siegler, Robert S., 28, 175, 176
silent learning, 31
slavery, 3
Smith, Nicholas, 121, 173
Snugglenumber, 75, 111
social conventions, 8
Sorooshian, Pam, 8, 176
Sousa, David A., 99, 176
Square One Television, 78, 114
standardized testing, 65
Strike It Out, 95
subitizing, 18
Subtraction War, 91
subtraction, mirror image of addition, 83
superficial understanding, 99

supplies
    card holder for young hands, 32
    cards, 11
    dice, 13
    dominoes, 13
    game boards, 12
    keeping a game box, 13
    subitizing cards, 18
    tokens, 13
Sven, 76, 112

T

Talking Math with Your Kids, 7, 171
Tanton, James, xiii, 54, 84, 176
Target Ten, 118
Target X, 119
teaching
    differentiation, 6
    games in the classroom, 5, 105
    ideal strategy, 3
    listening to kids, 6
    Math Wars, 147
    mental math strategies, 100, 116
    Nix the Tricks, 152
    posing questions, 65
    save the world, 156
    speed games, 5
    struggle for balance, 99, 149
    workbook syndrome, 147
Ten Cards, 133
Tens Concentration, 85
Tens Go Fish, 60
The Canterbury Puzzles, 103, 133, 171
"The Case of the Mysterious Story
    Problem", ix, 172
thinking process, 81
Thirty-One, 103
Tiguous, 122
Tiguous-Tac-Toe, 124
times-nine trick, 148
"Tiny Math Games", 22, 69, 108, 175
tokens, types of, 13
too easy, 5

About
the Author

DENISE GASKINS ENJOYS MATH, AND she delights in sharing that joy with young people. "Math is not just rules and rote memory," she says. "Math is like ice cream, with more flavors than you can imagine. And if all you ever do is textbook math, that's like eating broccoli-flavored ice cream."

A veteran homeschooling mother of five, Denise has taught or tutored mathematics at every level from pre-K to undergraduate physics "which," she explains, "at least in the recitation class I taught, was just one story problem after another. What fun!"

Now she writes the popular Let's Play Math blog and manages the monthly Playful Math Education blog carnival.

A Note from Denise

I hope you enjoyed this book and found new ideas that will help your children enjoy learning. I'd love to connect with you online and to hear your family's experiences with mathematical play.

If you believe this book is worth sharing, please consider posting a review on Goodreads, LibraryThing, or your favorite bookseller's website. An honest review is the highest compliment you can pay to any author, and your comments help fellow readers discover good books.

Thank you!

—DENISE GASKINS

LET'S CONNECT ONLINE: DeniseGaskins.com, LetsPlayMath@gmail.com

Books by Denise Gaskins

tabletopacademy.net/playful-math-books

"Denise has gathered up a treasure trove of living math resources for busy parents. If you've ever struggled to see how to make math come alive beyond your math curriculum (or if you've ever considered teaching math without a curriculum), you'll want to check out this book."

— KATE SNOW, AUTHOR OF *MULTIPLICATION FACTS THAT STICK*

Let's Play Math:
How Families Can Learn Math
Together — and Enjoy It

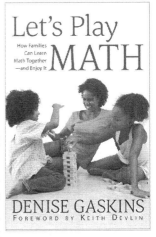

Transform your child's experience of math!

Even if you struggled with mathematics in school, you can help your children enjoy learning and prepare them for academic success.

Author Denise Gaskins makes it easy with this mixture of math games, low-prep project ideas, and inspiring coffee-chat advice from a veteran homeschooling mother of five. Drawing on more than thirty years' teaching experience, Gaskins provides helpful tips for parents with kids from preschool to high school, whether your children learn at home or attend a traditional classroom.

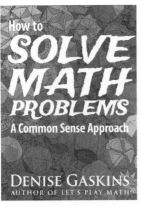

Don't let your children suffer from the epidemic of math anxiety. Pick up a copy of *Let's Play Math*, and start enjoying math today.

Want to help your kids learn math? Claim your free copy of Denise's 24-page problem-solving booklet, and sign up to hear about new books, revisions, and sales or other promotions.

TabletopAcademy.net/Subscribe

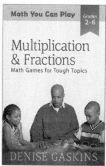

The *Math You Can Play* Series

You'll love these math games because they give your child a strong foundation for mathematical success.

By playing these games, you strengthen your child's intuitive understanding of numbers and build problem-solving strategies. Mastering a math game can be hard work. But kids do it willingly because it's fun.

Math games prevent math anxiety. Games pump up your child's mental muscles, reduce the fear of failure, and generate a positive attitude toward mathematics.

So what are you waiting for? Clear off a table, grab a deck of cards, and let's play some math.

Under Construction: The *Playful Math Singles* Series

The Playful Math Singles from Tabletop Academy Press are short, topical books featuring clear explanations and ready-to-play activities.

Word Problems from Literature features story problems for elementary and middle school students based on family-favorite books such as *Mr. Popper's Penguins* and *The Hobbit*. Step by step solutions demonstrate how bar model diagrams can help children reason their way to the answer.

70+ Things To Do with a Hundred Chart shows you how to take your child on a mathematical adventure through playful, practical activities. Who knew math could be so much fun?

More titles coming soon. Watch for them at your favorite online bookstore.

Fantasy Novels by Teresa Gaskins

The Riddled Stone Series

Banished

Hunted

Betrayed

Reviews

"People who like medieval-style fantasies with wraiths, spirits, and even an attacking swamp tree will enjoy the story. The excitement, adventure, and suspense will easily keep the reader's attention."
—Wayne S. Walker, Home School Book Review

"The setting is a world of 'light' magic. Magic is rare, constrained, and follows a sort of logic, which may or not be fully understood by the people in the world. I like the way in which this sets up plot connections and forces things to happen for a reason, rather than deus ex machina or authorial patronus."
—Phanwadee, online reader review

"Intriguing … There are many new languages unearthed, magic uncovered, and creatures unleashed … I enjoyed the book and I am absolutely amazed at how such a young author can write so well. I definitely see her going far in her writing career, and I can't wait to see what stories she publishes next."
—Tia at HomeschoolLiterature.com

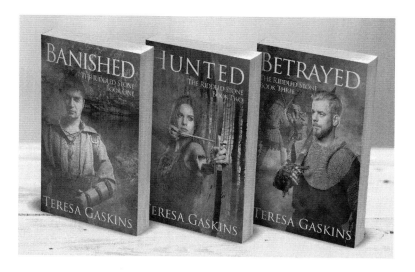

Banished: Haunted by dreams. On a quest for answers.

Christopher Fredrico liked the quiet life of a scholar-in-training. Plenty of spare time to spend with his friends. But the night Crown Prince Tyler came to dinner, everything changed.

Falsely accused of stealing a magical artifact and banished under threat of death, Chris leaves the only home he knows.

But as he and his friends travel towards the coast, they find a riddle that may save a kingdom—or cost them their lives.

Hunted: She tried to warn them. They wouldn't listen.

As a child, Terrin of Xell barely escaped a spirit from the Dark Forest. She knows better than to rely on magic. But with her schoolmate Chris accused of a magical crime he didn't commit, she couldn't let him face banishment alone.

So Terrin gets caught up in Chris's quest to recover an ancient relic, with only magic to guide them.

Naturally, everything goes wrong.

What lurks in the shadows, hunting Terrin and her friends? Or did the magic itself turn against them?

Betrayed: How can a knight fight magic?

Trained by the greatest knight in North Raec, Sir Arnold Fredrico dreamed of valiant deeds. Save the damsel. Serve the king.

Dreams change. Now the land teeters at the brink of war. As a fugitive with a price on his head, Arnold struggles to protect his friends.

But his enemy wields more power than the young knight can imagine.

Printed in Great Britain
by Amazon